Laboratory
Raman
Spectroscopy

LABORATORY RAMAN SPECTROSCOPY

DENNIS P. STROMMEN
Carthage College
Kenosha, Wisconsin

KAZUO NAKAMOTO
Marquette University
Milwaukee, Wisconsin

A Wiley-Interscience Publication
JOHN WILEY & SONS
New York • Chichester • Brisbane • Toronto • Singapore

Library of Congress Cataloging in Publication Data

Strommen, Dennis P. 1938–
    Laboratory Raman spectroscopy.

    "A Wiley-Interscience publication."
    Includes index.
    1. Raman spectroscopy. I. Nakamoto, Kazuo
II. Title.
    QD96.R34N35 1984   543'.08584   84-10322
    ISBN 0-471-81323-0

Printed in the United States of America

10 9 8 7 6 5 4 3 2 1

Preface

Although there are numerous excellent texts that deal with the theory of Raman spectroscopy, we are unaware of any currently published work that presents a "nuts and bolts" approach to the field. Unlike obtaining an infrared spectrum, the process of recording Raman data is rather involved and may be correctly described as requiring a good deal of artistry. Frequency calibration and sample orientation are not trivial matters; slit programs that maintain constant energy throughput are not available; and since the spectra are obtained from a single beam instrument, detector response becomes important. Over the past 18 years we have had occasion to confront all of these problems as well as many others. We have dealt with these troubles, as have most Raman spectroscopists, by simple trial and error. Now that Raman spectroscopy has been shown to be a powerful tool in many areas of chemistry and biochemistry, we see a dramatic increase in the number of users, many of whom are not Raman spectroscopists by trade. It is our intent that this volume serve as a basic laboratory manual for the chemist who wishes to measure Raman spectra under a variety of experimental conditions.

The selection of topics is somewhat arbitrary and based on our experience as to the relevance of the various techniques. We have made a conscious effort to minimize the volume of written words in this text while maximizing the amount of useful data. As a result, we do not include any justification for the rules and methods described herein. We also omitted even a simple explanation of the Raman effect since it is given in many textbooks and review articles.

We wish to express our sincere thanks to Profs. D. F. Shriver (Northwestern University), T. Loehr (Oregon Graduate Center), J. Kincaid (Marquette University), B. Pollard (Marquette University), J. Kitagawa (Institute for Molecular Science), and Messrs. J. Shane (Spectra-Physics), W. Walker (Spex Industries), and R. Grayzel (Instruments, S. A.) for their valuable comments and criticism. Our thanks also go to Dr. R. Czernuszewicz, who recorded the Raman spectra shown in Chapter 5 and assisted in production of the figures, and to Mr. Carrol Hanson, who photographed most of these spectra. We would also like to thank Drs. T. Watanabe and H. Oshio and Messrs K. Bajdor and A. Bruha of Marquette University for proofreading the manuscript.

DENNIS P. STROMMEN
KAZUO NAKAMOTO

Milwaukee, Wisconsin
Kenosha, Wisconsin
December 1984

v

Contents

CHAPTER 1. THE RAMAN SPECTROPHOTOMETER

1.1. BASIC COMPONENTS

Raman spectrophotometers consist of five basic components:

1. A source, usually a CW gas laser.

2. A sample illuminating system.

3. A sample holder.

4. A double or triple monochromator.

5. A signal processing system—including a photomultiplier tube,

   an amplification system, an output device.

Figure 1.1 is a schematic of one possible arrangement of these parts.

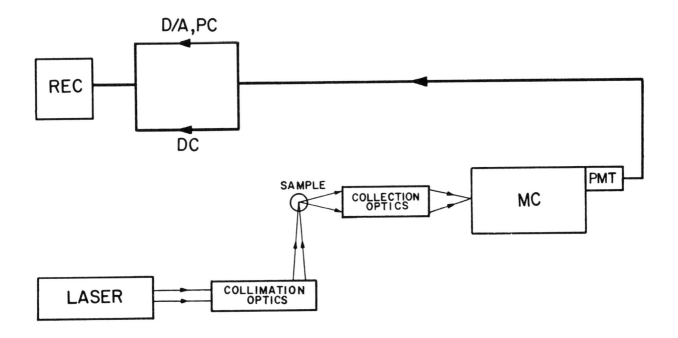

Figure 1.1. Layout of a typical Raman spectrophotometer: MC, monochromator;
         PM, photomultiplier; DC, direct current amplification; D/A,
         digital to analog converter; PC, photon counting detector;
         REC, recorder.

Currently there are a wide variety of modifications of the system depicted in the figure, including the addition of computers to both control the instrument and collect the data. However, the basic configuration remains unchanged in the majority of applications. This chapter is devoted to brief descriptions of each of the major parts of the basic spectrophotometer system with the exception of the sample holder which will be treated in Chapter 2. Suggested maintenance procedures will be given where appropriate.

1.2. SOURCES

CW Gas Lasers

The three most common gas lasers employed in Raman spectrophotometers are the Ar-ion, Kr-ion, and He-Ne lasers. Figure 1.2 depicts the components of a simple gas laser. Table 1.1 contains the major wavelengths at which each of these lasers can be operated, and Tables 1.2 to 1.4 contain lists of plasma lines which can be used for frequency calibration (vide infra).

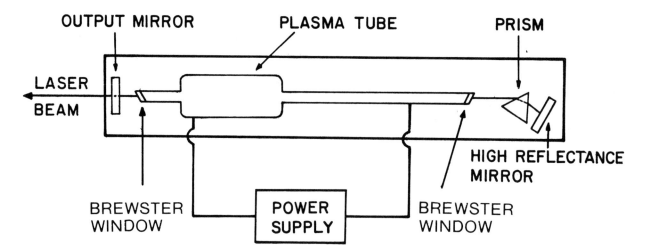

Figure 1.2. Schematic of a typical gas laser.

Table 1.1. Some Lasing Lines of Typical Gas Lasers

in the Visible Region

Laser	Wavelength in Air(nm)	Wavenumber in Air(cm^{-1})	Typical Power(mW)
Ar-ion[a]	457.9(violet)	21838.8	300
	465.8	21468.4	130
	472.7	21155.1	250
	476.5(blue)	20986.4	600
	488.0(blue)	20491.8	1300
	496.5	20141.0	600
	501.7(green)	19932.2	300
	514.5(green)	19436.3	1700
	528.7(yellow-green)	18914.3	300
Kr-ion[b]	476.2	20999.6	60
	482.5	20725.4	45
	520.8	19201.2	90
	530.9	18835.9	200
	568.2	17599.4	200
	647.1(red)	15453.6	500
	676.4	14784.2	120
	752.5	13289.0	100
	799.3	12510.9	30
He-Ne[c]	632.8(red)	15802.8	50

a. Power value for Spectra-Physics Model 164-08.

b. Power value for Spectra-Physics Model 164-01.

c. Power value for Spectra-Physics Model 125A.

Table 1.2. Principal Plasma Lines in the Argon Ion Laser

Wavelength in Air (nm)	Relative Intensity	Wavelength in Air (nm)	Relative Intensity
487.9860	5000	569.1650	27
488.9033	200	572.4325	23
490.4753	130	573.95207	16
493.3206	970	577.2326	69
494.2915	14	578.6560	16
495.5111	10	581.2746	49
496.5073	960	584.3781	18
497.2157	330	587.0443	12
500.9334	1500	588.26250	11
501.7160	620	588.85851	18
506.2036	1400	591.20861	38
509.0496	10	592.88124	10
514.1790	360	595.0905	11
514.5319	1000	598.5920	23
516.2745	8	598.9339	20
516.5774	38	603.21291	57
517.6233	41	604.32254	37
521.6816	20	604.4468	14
528.6895	150	604.6894	14
530.5690	12	604.9072	14
539.7522	18	605.93735	15
540.2604	11	607.7431	11
540.7348	12	610.3546	91
545.4307	19	611.4929	< 1750
549.5876	14	612.3368	100
549.8185	14	613.8660	97
550.0334	14	617.2290	1400
555.4050	22	618.7136	26
555.87031	30	623.9713	26
557.25428	12	624.3125	590
557.7689	18	632.4414	16
557.8518	11	638.47189	11
560.67341	48	639.6614	14
562.5684	14	639.9215	160
563.5882	14	641.63075	50
565.07054	29	643.7604	27
565.4450	27	644.1908	22
567.2952	22	644.3858	16

Source: N. C. Craig and I. W. Levin, Appl. Spectrosc., 33, 475 (1979).
Reproduced with permission.

4

Table 1.3. Principal Plasma Lines in the Krypton Ion Laser

Wavelength in Air (nm)	Relative Intensity	Wavelength in Air (nm)	Relative Intensity	Wavelength in Air (nm)	Relative Intensity
521.60	350	591.17	110	731.05	80
522.49	20	596.75	100	733.78	60
522.95	600	599.22	1000	736.16	90
527.65	220	601.00	90	737.30	60
530.87	2300	602.24	200	740.70	800
532.28	200	603.72	10	743.58	400
533.24	2000	609.45	50	744.38	150
534.68	300	611.96	70	748.68	280
535.55	80	616.88	160	749.36	180
541.84	200	630.37	160	751.26	400
543.86	400	631.28	10	752.45	600
544.63	900	639.11	100	755.57	180
546.82	1100	640.98	70	756.54	250
549.95	450	641.66	150	758.74	550
552.29	1050	624.02	700	760.15	600
555.30	400			768.52	400
556.22	200	647.09	250	769.45	250
556.86	1000	651.09	430	773.57	200
557.03	550	657.01	1000	775.07	200
563.50	1400	660.30	160	778.94	130
565.04	250	662.50	30	781.25	250
566.99	300	662.86	160	782.60	450
567.28	570	663.50	110	783.58	190
567.45	400	664.45	100	784.07	520
568.19	3500	665.25	100	785.48	500
569.03	2000	668.40	60	790.76	120
569.41	400	676.44	330	791.01	190
569.99	400	677.12	100	791.45	70
571.72	180	687.08	110	793.14	130
575.30	1000	694.41	30	797.36	100
577.14	1700	707.40	100	799.32	700
577.80	400	713.40	170	799.80	300
586.07	270	721.31	600	801.86	110
587.09	750	728.98	900	805.95	600

Source: C. Julien and C. Hirlimann, J. Raman Spectrosc., 9, 62 (1980).
Reproduced with permission.

Table 1.4 Principal Plasma Lines from a He-Ne Laser

Wavelength in Air (nm)	Relative Intensity	Wavelength in Air (nm)	Relative Intensity
638.299	53	706.519	31
640.108	>100	717.394	4
640.975	31	724.517	5
644.472	30	728.135	11
650.653	50	748.887	0.5
659.895	41	753.577	0.4
667.815 } 667.828	91	754.405	0.3
671.704	36	777.730	5
692.947	19	794.318	0.1
		813.641	0.2

Source: Reproduced with permission of Spex Industries.

In Tables 1.1 to 1.4 the values are expressed as wavelengths and wave-numbers in air. The difference between $\Delta\upsilon$(air) and $\Delta\upsilon$(vac) is usually less than 1 cm^{-1} and can be ignored in Raman spectroscopy. When molecular constants are calculated from absolute Raman frequencies, υ(air) must be converted to υ(vac).[*]

Plasma lines can be problematic if proper filtering techniques are not employed (see Section 4.4). Figure 1.3 shows a spectrum of the plasma lines emitted by a detuned Ar-ion laser.[+]

In order to obtain the maximum performance from a laser, the following suggestions are made. The room where the laser is kept should be as dust-free as possible, and smoking should not be allowed at any time. It is recommended to purge each end of the plasma tube by a dry gas (nitrogen or air) to minimize deposit formation on the Brewster windows. Figure 1.4 illustrates a simple gas purge system which consists of a pump (or a tank), a filter and a flow gauge.[‡] Teflon tubing should be used throughout; flexible tubing such as polypropylene contains significant amounts of plasticizer which may deposit on Brewster windows.

---

[*] G. Strey, Spectrochim. Acta, 25A, 163 (1969).

[+] This spectrum was recorded in our laboratory using a Spectra-Physics Model 164-08 Ar-ion laser.

[‡] The "Silent Giant" air pump is available at local pet shops. The "Petro-Sorb" MDY4463-CE-4 can be obtained from the Pall Trinity Micro Corporation, Cortland, NY 13045 with replacement cartridges MCS 4463-CE, and the "RMA-2-SSV (0.1 to 1.0 CFH)" from Dwyer Instruments, Michigan City, IN 46360.

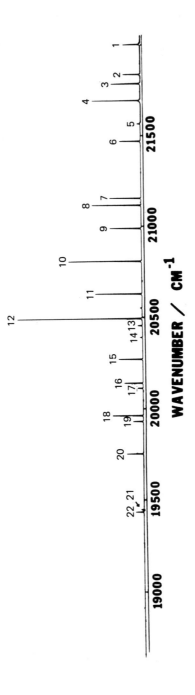

Figure 1.3. Spectrum of plasma lines emitted by a Spectra-Physics Model 164-08 Ar-ion laser. (The numbers refer to values tabulated in Table 3.2.) All lines mirror, slits 50/100/50, range 5 K, scan speed 25 cm^{-1}/min, period 0.1 sec, chart speed 1/2 in./min.

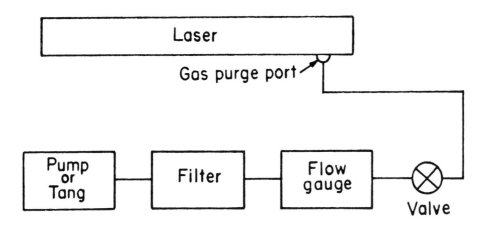

Figure 1.4. Gas purge system.

Usually lasers are designed to use ordinary tap water which flows through the unit, but closed-loop cooling systems can be used as well. In any case a minimum flow (which depends on the laser model) with a constant differential pressure across the unit is required. If the water pressure is inadequate, pumps are available to increase the flow rate (for recommendation, see the laser operation manual). Also, since the cooling water is in contact with the plasma tube anode and can be considered to be at that potential, a sufficiently deionized water should preferably be used.

Humidity during the summer time can be a problem since water condensation has been known to cause a shorting in the power supply. Whenever water condensation occurs on the faucet pipe, laser operation should be stopped. An air-conditioned room is an ideal location for the laser. If one is not available, the problem can be alleviated by cooling the laser with a mixture of warm and cold water rather than just cold water.

Regular changing of the water filter is essential.* Buildup of water deposits results in inefficient cooling of the laser and significant shortening of laser lifetime. We recommend that the water filter be replaced when it has clogged most of the way, which can be detected by visual inspection.

In addition to these precautions we recommend the use of minimum laser power to prolong the lifetime of the plasma tube. For example, the average lifetime of the plasma tube of Spectra-Physics Model 164 Ar-ion laser is about 1200 hours under normal use (20 amps). With extreme care it is possible to prolong the life to as long as three or four years. Even when no spectral measurements are carried out, lasers should be used regularly (every 10 days or so) for an hour to discharge gases adsorbed on glass surfaces.

The following materials are available as a kit from Spectra-Physics:[+]

   1. Forced air supply

   2. Lens tissue

   3. Cotton swabs (Q-tips)

   4. Hemostats

   5. Acetone (CH_3COCH_3)--spectroscopic grade

---

* Water filters may be purchased from Oargreen Sales Engineering Corp., 1224 Capitol Drive, Addision, IL 60101 (specify Filterlite, Silverscreen 4-34) or Great Lakes Filter Media, 5151 Loraine, Detroit, MI 48208.
+ Spectra-Physics, 1245 Terra Bella, Mountain View, CA 94042.

6. Methanol (CH_3OH)—spectroscopic grade

7. Hydrogen peroxide (H_2O_2) 5% solution

8. Oakite 33 (proprietary detergent)[*]

9. Deionized or distilled water

10. Pre-rinse solution—made up of

    1 part nitric acid (HNO_3)

    19 parts deionized water

    17 parts methanol

11. Calcium carbonate—primary standard powder 600 [+] mesh

    (per American Chemical Society specification), Mallinckrodt

    4071 or 4072 or equivalent

12. Micro Detergent (proprietary detergent)[+]

---

[*] Oakite 33 can be purchased from Oakite Products, Inc., 50 Valley Road, Berkely Heights, NJ 07922.

[+] Micro Detergent can be purchased from International Products Corp., P. O. Box 118, Trenton, NJ 08601.

One of the major causes of power loss is the accumulation of dust and films on the Brewster windows and mirrors. The laser power for a given current (e.g., 100 MW at 20 amp) should be monitored on a regular basis (daily, weekly, etc). When a 5 to 10% reduction in power is noted for the given current level, then the following procedure, which is suggested by Spectra-Physics, should be implemented. Normally only Steps 1, 2, and 3 are necessary.

1. Blow away dust with forced air (item 1 of preceding list of materials.

2. Use lens tissue (item 2) and acetone (item 5) to clean windows as per standard procedure.*

3. Repeat Step 2 with methanol (item 6), and follow with an acetone wipe.

4. Using 5% H_2O_2 (item 7) on cotton swab (item 3) clean entire window surface with circular scrubbing motion, followed by methanol wipe.

5. a. Using Oakite 33 (item 8) on a cotton swab, clean entire window surface with circular scrubbing motion.

   b. Rinse windows using a cotton swab and deionized water (item 9). Repeat this step three times using a fresh swab each time.

   c. Follow with methanol wipe.

---

* The procedure is given in the laser instruction manual.

6. a. Use pre-rinse solution (item 10) on a cotton swab to wet the entire window.

   b. Dip a fresh cotton swab, wet with pre-rinse solution, lightly into calcium carbonate powder (item 11). Scrub window for about 30 seconds (Calcium carbonate should have consistency of tooth paste.)

   c. Dip a dry cotton swab into calcium carbonate, and scrub window. This will dry as paste.

   d. Rinse again with pre-rinse solution on a cotton swab.

   e. Using Micro Detergent (item 12) on a cotton swab; clean entire surface with circular scrubbing motion.

   f. Use deionized water to rinse three times as in Step 5b.

   g. Use lens tissue and methanol for final wipe.

Safety glasses should be used whenever possible since the laser beam can do serious damage to the eye. The operator should be aware that reflections of the laser beam as well as of the primary beam are hazardous. Of course the high voltages employed in laser operation require that the operator exercise extreme care to avoid physical contact with the laser housing and the power supply. We recommend signs be posted to this effect.

Dye Lasers

The range of wavelengths available for Raman excitation can be
extended and made nearly continuous throught the use of dye lasers.
There are three basic types of dye lasers: CW gas laser pumped, pulsed
laser pumped and flash lamp pumped. All of these require relatively large
volumes of organic dyes. Figure 1.5 shows the range capability of the
Spectra-Physics Model 375 dye laser.

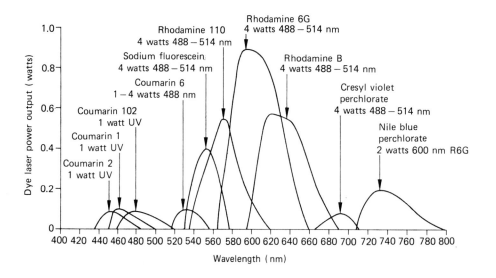

Figure 1.5. Output powers and wavelengths obtainable from a Model 375
           Spectra-Physics dye laser pumped by an Ar-ion laser (repro-
           duced by permission of Spectra-Physics).

Similar ranges are available from flash lamp pumped instruments. Band widths are typically about 1 cm^{-1} but can be reduced to 0.1 cm^{-1} with the use of fine tuning etalons. In the following we present recipes for the preparation of dye solutions that can be used with CW gas laser pumped systems.

Rhodamine 6G (580 to 640 nm)

Step 1: Dissolve 0.48 g of Rodamine 6G in ca. 50 ml of CH$_3$OH (use minimum amount).

Step 2: Add to 500 ml of ethylene glycol, and mix completely by stirring for at least one hour.

Step 3: Filter the solutions through filter paper to remove any undissolved particles.

Step 4: Renew solution every 100 watt-hours.

Rhodamine B (610 to 660 nm)

Step 1: Dissolve 2 g of Rodamine B in 30 ml of CH$_3$OH.

Step 2: Circulate 1200 ml of ethylene glycol in the pump.

Step 3: Add Solution 1 to 2 while circulating, and mix completely.

Step 4: Maximize laser power by adding a solution of one g Rhodamine B in 15 ml of CH$_3$OH.

Sodium Flouorescein (540 to 570 nm)

Step 1: Dissolve 1 g of sodium fluorescein in 10 ml of
CH_3OH.

Step 2: Circulate 750 ml of ethylene glycol in the pump.

Step 3: Add Solution 1 to 2 while circulating.

Step 4: Add 2.5 ml of COT (cyclooctatetraene) to the solution
to maximize laser power.[*]

Step 5: This dye falls to 50% of its original power in just a
few hours.

The procedures for changing filters and dye solutions and cleaning the
nozzle are given in the operation manual of the dye laser.

1.3. SAMPLE ILLUMINATION

Because of the inherent weakness of the Raman effect, the laser beam
must be tightly focused within the sample, and the scattered radiation must
be efficiently collected. Fortunately focused beams on the order of a few
microns in diameter are readily obtainable.[+] Excitation of the sample and
collection of the scattered radiation may be accomplished by employing
numerous optical configurations. Two of the more common methods of illumination refered to as 90 and 180 degree scattering are depicted in Figures
1.6 and 1.7 respectively.

---

* CAUTION: Be sure to use proper ventilation techniques when using this
material.

+ J. P. Hendra, "Raman Instrumentation and Sampling" in Laboratory Methods
in Infrared Spectroscopy, R. G. J. Miller, ed., Heyden, London, 1972,
p. 234.

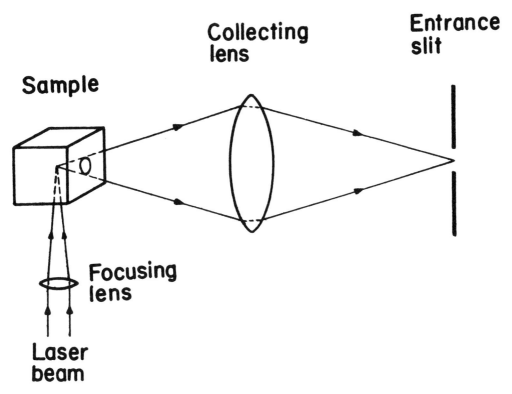

Figure 1.6. 90 degree scattering configuration.

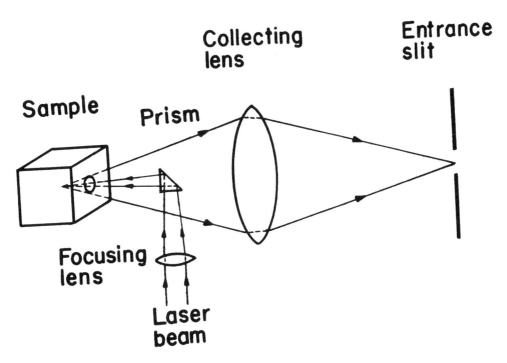

Figure 1.7. 180 degree scattering configuration. (A small front surface mirror may be used instead of a prism.)

The 90 degree scattering method is the one most commonly encountered in the Raman laboratory, although there are some distinct advantages associated with the 180 degree method (see Section 2.8).

For simplicity in each of the figures we have indicated that the scattered radiation is collected by a single lens. However, the collection optics may also vary widely as shown in Figures 1.8 and 1.9. Figure 1.8 employs a series of achromatic lenses, whereas Figure 1.9 avoids the use of collector mirror and thus avoids the use of lenses and their associated signal losses. The collector mirror has the advantage that, if properly coated, it is convenient for use in the ultraviolet region.

Crude focusing of the incoming laser beam may be achieved by removing the sample holder and observing the position of the focus by interposing a thin layer of lens paper in the beam. The focal point may be readily observed by moving the paper along the beam direction. The position of the focus then is adjusted by changing the position of the lens. The final adjustment of this lens is made by observing the effect of its position on a Raman signal. Considerable time may be saved if the laser-focusing lens is an achromat. Then the foregoing procedure does not need to be repeated when the laser wavelength is being changed. In either case the laser power should be kept at a minimum and <u>Care should be taken to protect eyes during the procedure.</u>

Positioning the image of the irradiated sample on the entrance slit of the monochromator is one of the most important and difficult tasks. A crude method involves the use of a small section of a 3 × 5 file card. Holding the section near the slit allows for visualization of the image on the card.

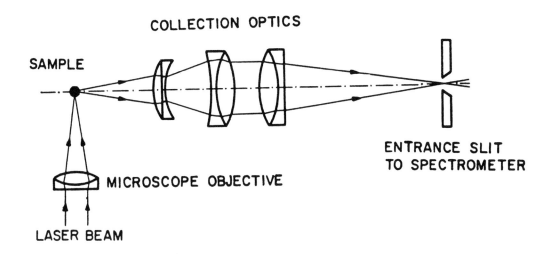

Figure 1.8. Collection optics with an achromatic lens system.

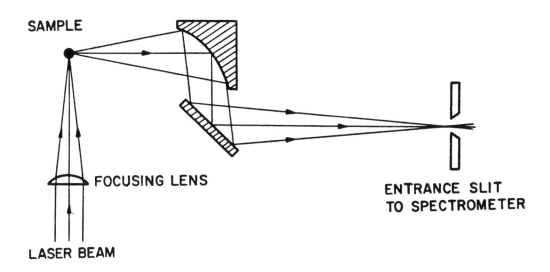

Figure 1.9. Collection optics with an eliptical collection mirror.

CAUTION: REFLECTIONS AT THIS POINT MAY SERIOUSLY DAMAGE YOUR EYES.
In the case of 90 degree scattering, a bright image is sometimes observed. This is not due to Raman scattering but to fluorescence (see Section 4.4) or reflections of the laser beam from glass, quartz, or the surface of the sample. During this process the room must be kept as dark as possible because the image is rather weak.

One must realize that only by investing the time to align the instrument properly can quality Raman data be obtained. Some operators have a tendency to take advantage of the electronics and forget correct sample handling. Meaningful data may easily be lost in this fashion. Therefore we recommend that the instrument output be optimized by employing a strongly scattering sample. In particular, for liquid sampling the 459 cm^{-1} band of CCl_4 can serve as a reference line for maximizing the signal. Once the best positions of the focusing lens, sample holder, and collection lens are found, the CCl_4 is replaced with the desired sample. Then the operator should scan manually with Caution throughout the region of expected Raman bands to find the strongest signal. The fine adjustments of the collection optics should be made by maximizing the signal from the sample. As a final word of caution, note that it is at this stage that one can easily damage the photomultiplier tube. Use the lowest possible laser power, and gradually increase it if necessary. However, the signal must always be kept below the maximum that is allowable for your particular instrument.

1.4. THE MONOCHROMATOR

Figures 1.10. a, b, and 1.11 depict schematics of typical double monochromators manufactured by Spex Industries and Instruments S. A.[*] Also available is a triple monochromator (Spex Triplemate) which has greater stray light rejection than double monochromators and allows the measurements of Raman lines which are extremely close to the Rayleigh line. The following discussion will refer particularly to Spex Model 1401 double monochromator.

There are three slits (four in Spex Model 1403) marked S1, S2, and S3. A significant difference between Raman and IR monochromators is that the slit settings in the former are made manually and are therefore constant throughout the scan. There are no slit programs to regulate energy throughout, and the resolution of the instrument will vary almost continuously. The maximum theoretical resolution (band pass, BP) that can be obtained may be calculated if dispersion data for the gratings are available through the use of the standard equation $BP = D_L^{-1} \times SW$, where D_L^{-1} is the inverse linear dispersion and SW is the mechanical slit width. Table 1.5 gives some typical data for the band pass and associated slit settings for various exciting lines. For example, slit settings of 90 μ when using 488.0 nm excitation allow a maximum resolution of 2.0 cm^{-1} [(1 cm^{-1}/45 μ) × 90 μ = 2.0 cm^{-1}]. However, the middle slit(s) S2 (and S3) which constitute(s) the exit from the first and the entrance to the second monochromator must be slightly wider in order to allow for small mechanical imperfections in the alignment of the two monochromators.

---

[*] Their addresses are, respectively, Spex Industries, Inc., 3880 Park Avenue, Metuchen, NJ 08840; Instruments S. A. Inc., 173 Essex Avenue, Metuchen, NJ 08840.

Figure 1.10. Spex double monochromator:

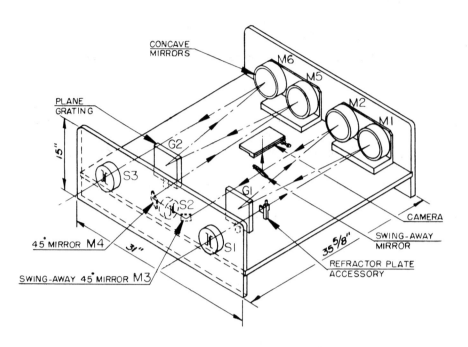

a. Models 1400 and 1401 (reproduced by permission of Spex Industries);

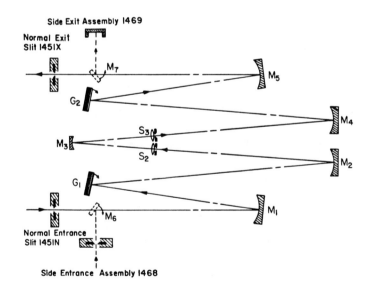

b. models 1403 and 1404.

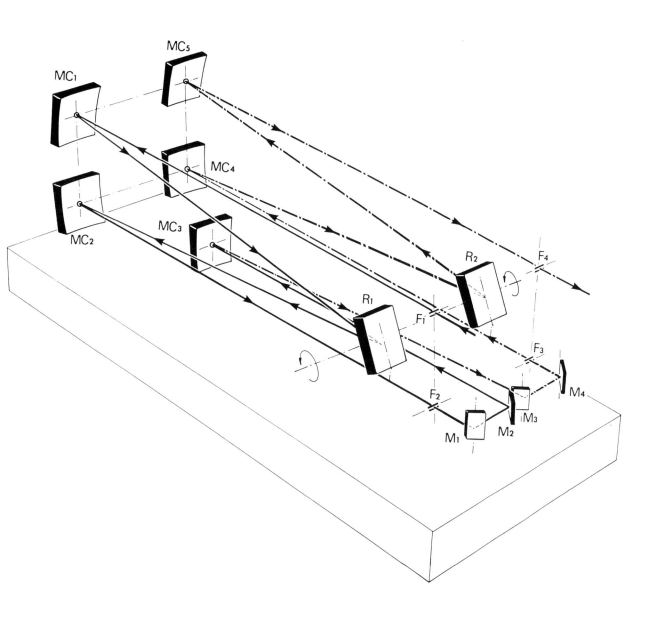

Figure 1.11. Instruments, S. A. Model U-1000 double monochromator
(reproduced by permission of Instruments, S. A.).

Table 1.5. Resolution and Slit Widths for Various Laser
Frequencies (Spex Model 1401 and Double 1403
Monochromators).

Resolution, cm^{-1} For Spex Model 1401 (1180 groove/mm)	Slit Width (μ) For Laser Frequencies					
	He-Ne 6328 Å (15802) $75\ \mu/cm^{-1}$	Ar 5145 Å (19435) $50\ \mu/cm^{-1}$	Ar 4880 Å (20492) $45\ \mu/cm^{-1}$	Kr 5208 Å (19200) $50\ \mu/cm^{-1}$	Kr 5682 Å (17600) $60\ \mu/cm^{-1}$	Kr 6471 Å (15454) $80\ \mu/cm^{-1}$
0.5	38	25	22	25	30	40
1.0	75	50	45	50	60	80
2.0	150	100	90	100	120	160
5.0	375	250	225	250	300	400
10.0	750	500	450	500	600	800
20.0	1500	1000	900	1000	1200	1600
40.0	3000	2000	1800	2000	2400	3200
For Spex Model 1403 (1800 grove/mm)	He-Ne 6328 Å (15802) $130\ \mu/cm^{-1}$	Ar 5145 Å (19435) $80\ \mu/cm^{-1}$	Ar 4880 Å (20492) $70\ \mu/cm^{-1}$	Kr 5208 Å (19200) $85\ \mu/cm^{-1}$	Kr 5682 Å (17600) $100\ \mu/cm^{-1}$	Kr 6471 Å (15454) $140\ \mu/cm^{-1}$
0.5	65	40	35	43	50	70
1.0	130	80	70	85	100	140
2.0	260	160	140	170	200	280
5.0	650	400	350	425	500	700

Note: The values are for first-order dispersion. If at any time second order
dispersion is used, double μ/cm^{-1} figures.

Table 1.6 gives some suggested settings for various desired resolutions and laser frequencies. The effect of changing the slit width is clearly seen in Figure 1.12 where the 459 cm^{-1} band of CCl_4 has been scanned at ~1 cm^{-1} and ~2 cm^{-1} band passes.* The signals were made comparable by decreasing the laser power in the latter case. It should be recalled that the signal is proportional to $(P_0) \times (SW)^2$, where P_0 is the incident power.

Mechanical backlash of the wavenumber reading is another problem that may be encountered when recording a spectrum on some instruments. In the case of the SPEX systems this is due to the fact that there must be clearance between the nut, the lead screw, and the rider attached to the cosecant arm.

Table 1.6. Suggested Slit Settings for Spex Model 1401 Monochromator

Resolution, cm^{-1}	Spectral Slit Width for Laser Frequency		
	6328 Å (15802 cm^{-1})	5145 Å (19435 cm^{-1})	4880 Å (20492 cm^{-1})
0.5	38-100-38	25-100-25	22-100-22
1.0	75-100-75	50-100-50	45-100-45
2.0	150-150-150	100-100-100	90-100-90
5.0	375-375-375	250-250-250	225-225-225
10.0	750-750-750	500-500-500	450-450-450
20.0	1500-1500-1500	1000-1000-1000	900-900-900

* Our Spex Model 1401 double monochromator has two identical Jarrell-Ash gratings, 1180 groove/mm, blazed at 5000 Å.

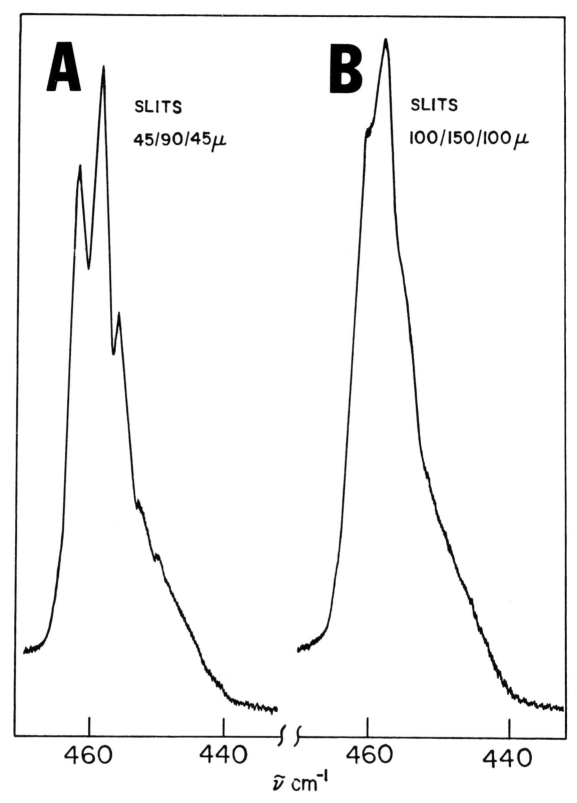

Figure 1.12. High resolution (<u>a</u>) and low resolution (<u>b</u>) scans of the 459 cm^{-1} band of CCl_4.

Rapid scanning can also cause distortion of the true spectral pattern as is shown in Figure 1.13. A simple way to detect this problem is to rerecord the spectrum at a slower scan speed and look for significant changes in the band patterns. The maximum scanning speed can be calculated and will be discussed in Section 4.2.

Finally, the temperature of the monochromator is important since band position may vary by as much as 3 cm^{-1}. Although the monochromator is normally thermostatted above room temperature, we have found that it is convenient to keep a laboratory thermometer in the monochromator for easy monitoring.

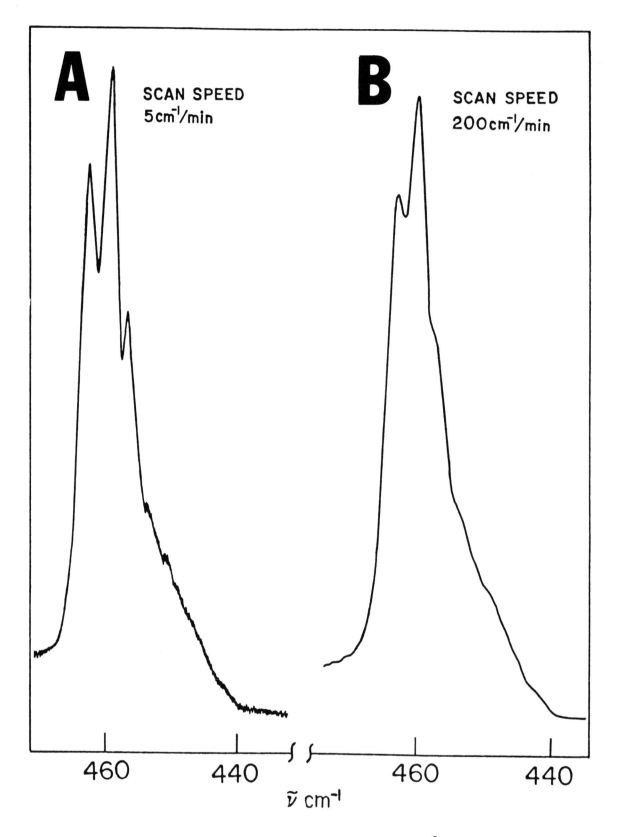

Figure 1.13. Slow (a) and fast (b) scans of the 459 cm^{-1} band of CCl$_4$.

1.5. SIGNAL-PROCESSING SYSTEMS

Photomultiplier Tube Operation

The detector usually employed in a Raman experiment is the photomultiplier(PM) tube. Although photodiode arrays, image vidicons, and photographic plates all give multichannel data, the photomultiplier is the detector usually encountered. An excellent reference detailing the fundamentals and choice of PM tubes is Photomultiplier Handbook: Theory, Design, Application.[*]

Every PM tube consists of a photocathode which emits electrons when photons strike it, via the external photoelectric effect, and a series of dynodes each of which emits a number of secondary electrons when struck by an electron. Figures 1-14a and b show typical PM tubes with the dynodes and the photocathodes interconnected by resistors (not shown) which distribute a high voltage among them. This high voltage which is nearly always applied negatively with respect to ground determines how many electrons are given off per electron striking a dynode and thus the total gain or multiplication of the tube. The quantum efficiency or probability of a primary electron being emitted from the photocathode surface is dependent on wavelength, and a graph of this function is shown in Figure 1.15 for a commonly used PM tube, the RCA 31034.

Proper care of the PM tube, its optics, and its housing are essential for good sensitivity. The primary limiting factor in PM tube performance is the noise due to background signal. This so-called "dark current" is primarily caused by spurious emission of electrons from the photocathode and

---

[*] RCA Electronics, Lancaster, PA, 1980.

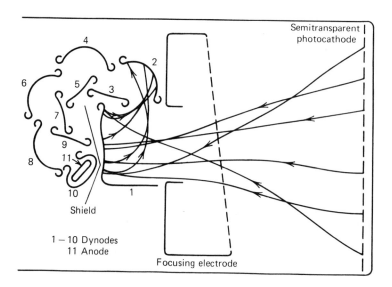

Figure 1.14.<u>a</u> An end-on photomultiplier structure utilizing a circular dynode arrangement (reproduced by permission of RCA);

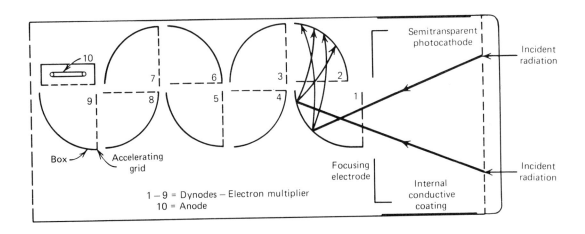

Figure 1.14.<u>b</u> Box-and-grid multiplier structure (reproduced by permission of RCA).

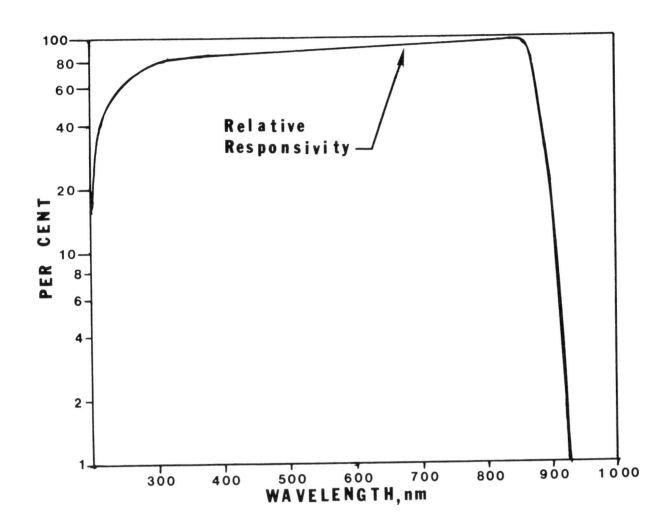

Figure 1.15. Photomultiplier response curve (RCA 31034A).

dynodes and by dielectric leakage across the PM tube base pins and resistor chain. To reduce these spurious emissions, a large portion of which are of thermionic origin, the tube is usually thermoelectrically cooled via the Peltier effect so that the weak Raman signal may be easily measured. As a result of cooling, condensation of water in the lens system just in front of the tube and in the base is not uncommon. If this problem occurs, the detector system may be disassembled and dried under vacuum in a darkened room.

When reassembling the system, the signal should be maximized using adjustment screws on the mounting of the PM tube while monitoring the Raman signal of CCl_4 at 459 cm^{-1}. The photocathode of any PM tube should be shielded from light, particularly when the high voltage is applied. Unfortunately there are times when Rayleigh scatter from the excitation source is inadvertently allowed to strike the detector. This results in a drastic increase in the dark signal. Thus extreme caution should be exercised when scanning close to the Rayleigh line or other strong lines (see Chapter 3). If permanent damage has not been done to the photocathode, the background signal and its accompanying noise will steadily decrease over a period of a few days to the normal levels.

Direct Current Amplification Systems

Direct current amplification systems can be employed to record the Raman signal coming from the detector by averaging the pulses of electrons over time. The photomultiplier generates currents that are directly proportional to the light intensity over the range 0.1 nanoamp, the dark current level, to 10 microamp. Raman signals are generally in the range of 1 to 100 nanoamp, and therefore an extremely sensitive current to voltage amplifier, sometimes called a picoameter or electrometer, is required to quantify them. Background signals which do not originate in the Raman effect (e.g., fluorescence generated by the sample) can be problematic and "wash out" the Raman signal. This unwanted background can sometimes be eliminated by the use of a zero suppression control which applies a "bucking" or offset potential to the amplifier system. However, this approach does not eliminate noise carried on the background signal and so is of limited use for backgrounds stronger than about three times the Raman signal.

An important consideration is the reduction of noise in the recorded spectrum. With DC electronics this is accomplished by placing a filter between the amplifier and output device. Many commercial amplifier systems have a variable time constant filter built in. Increasing the time constant decreases the signal-carried noise and also the response time of the electronics. This necessitates reduction of the monochromator scanning speed in order to prevent peak deformation and loss of resolution (see Section 4.4).

Photon-Counting Systems

Photon-counting systems detect the electron pulses caused by individual photons reaching the photocathode. The real advantage of photon counting is that a substantial fraction of the dark signal can be electronically discriminated from photon pulses so that the ultimate sensitivity of the detector can be increased, typically, by a factor of 10 over a DC system. A disadvantage exists in that the maximum signal is limited to a photon count rate at which photon events do not overlap. In practice, this "pulse pileup" limit is around 150×10^6 photon sec^{-1} which corresponds to about 800 nanoamp.

Thus this system is applicable to all but the strongest of Raman signals.

In the photon-counting mode the operator must coordinate integration time with monochromator scan rate or interval to maintain optimum resolution. For proper operation of photon-counting systems, careful optimization of the PM tube's high voltage and pulse discriminator levels based on signal-to-noise ratios must be performed for each Raman apparatus. The results of this procedure will determine the day-to-day settings of these controls.

CHAPTER 2. SAMPLING TECHNIQUES

A variety of sampling techniques have been developed to suit the particular needs of individual investigators. Some of them require only simple Raman cells and accessories, whereas others involve complicated and rather expensive sampling devices. In this chapter we will describe some of the sampling techniques designed for the 90 degree scattering geometry (Figure 1.6) which is used by the majority of workers. Sampling techniques involving the 180 degree geometry (Fig. 1.7.) will be presented in Section 2.7.

If the sample is colorless, its Raman spectrum can be measured easily by sample irradiation with a laser beam whose wavelength is in the visible region (normal Raman scattering). If the sample is colored and/or absorbs the laser beam, it may be decomposed by local heating. In this case, several remedies are available in addition to the simple reduction of laser power. These are: (1) changing the laser wavelength, (2) defocusing the laser beam on the sample, (3) diluting the sample concentration in a pellet or in solution, (4) cooling the sample, (5) rotating the sample, and (6) rotating or oscillating of the laser on a fixed beam sample. These techniques are extremely important because resonance Raman spectra thus obtained provide valuable information about electronic spectra, excited states, and vibrational assignments.[*] In the following section typical techniques that are currently used will be described briefly. Only original references will be cited for special techniques.

---

* For example, see D. P. Strommen and K. Nakamoto, J. Chem. Educ., 54, 474 (1977).

2.1. TECHNIQUES FOR COLORLESS COMPOUNDS

The great advantage Raman has over infrared spectroscopy is that the sample can be contained or sealed in a glass (Pyrex) tube because Raman scattered light in the visible region is not absorbed by glass. Thus Raman spectra of hygroscopic, corrosive, or oxygen-sensitive compounds can be measured by sealing them in glass tubing or bottles. It should be noted, however, that some glass tubing gives rise to fluorescence or spikes if contaminated with rare earth salts. Raman spectra of aqueous solutions can be measured easily because water is a very weak Raman scatterer.

Gases

Normally the sample gas is contained in glass tubing of diameter 1~2 cm and thickness~1 nm. Figure 2.1 shows a typical setup for a gaseous sample. If necessary, the gas may be sealed in small capillary tubing whose diameter is slightly larger than that of the laser beam (~1 mm). For weak Raman scatters an external resonating setup is needed to increase their Raman intensity by multiple passing of the laser beam through the sample. A double-pass system is shown in Figure 2.1.

Liquids

Liquid samples may be sealed in ampoules, tubing, or capillaries, depending on the amount of the sample available. For micro quantities (~10^{-9} liter), capillaries as small as 0.5 − 0.1 mm bore and~1 mm in length have been used.[*] Figure 2.2a shows a typical setup for a liquid sample in a capillary. A large cylindrical cell (~1 cm in diameter, ~1 cm high) is also

---

*S. K. Freeman and D. O. Landon, Spex Speaker, 8, 4 (1968).

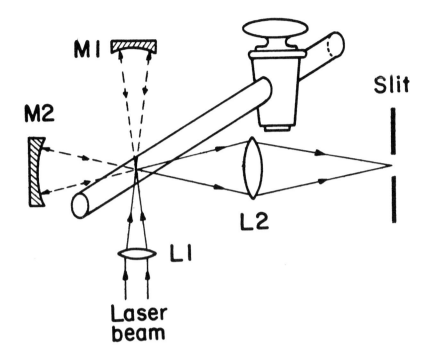

Figure 2.1. Gas cell with external resonating mirrors.

Figure 2.2.<u>a</u> Typical capillary cell;   Figure 2.2.<u>b</u> Cylindrical Cell.

available (Figure 2.2.b). The use of the latter reduces local heating effects and allows more accurate determination of depolarization ratios (see Section 4.3). If the solution contains particulate matter, strong spike noise may appear in the spectrum.

Solids

Powdered samples may be packed in ampoules or capillaries, depending on the amount of the sample available, and their Raman spectra are measured in exactly the same manner as liquid samples. Another useful technique involves irradiation of a pellet (see Figure 2.3) prepared by the following procedure: First, using a standard KBr pellet apparatus, 200 mg of KBr power is compressed at $\sim$ 6000 lb/sq in. to provide a support for the sample. This will allow the use of very small amounts of sample. Then $\sim$ 50 mg of the ground sample is evenly spread over the top of the KBr while still in the die. If necessary, an internal standard such as KNO_3 or K_2SO_4 (see Section 3.2) may be mixed with the sample at this point. If the sample is decomposed by local heating, we

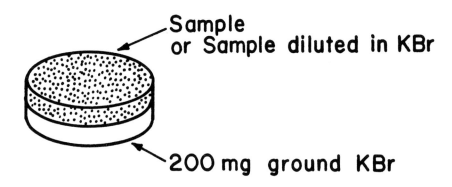

Figure 2.3. Laminar pellet for front surface Raman scattering.

recommend diluting the sample with KBr powder. The apparatus is reassembled, and a pressure of about 17,000 lb/sq in. is applied for 30 sec. The pellet is removed from the die, and the spectrum is taken off the surface.

Occasionally, it is possible to obtain large single crystals. In this case, a detailed analysis of polarizability tensors can be done by measuring polarized Raman spectra along the three principal axes of the crystal.[*] A goniometer head such as that used for X-ray work is employed for accurate setting of the crystal.

2.2. TECHNIQUES FOR COLORED COMPOUNDS

If a sample is colored, efficient absorption of the laser radiation may occur, causing local heating and sometimes sample decomposition. To minimize this problem, the simplest approach is to defocus the laser beam at the sample. Although there is some loss of signal, the power density per unit area will be greatly reduced, and thus there will be less local heating.

---

[*] S. P. S. Porto, Spex Speaker, 8, 2 (1968). S. P. S. Porto, T. A. Giordmaine, and T. C. Damen, Phys. Rev., 147, 608, (1966).

One may also insert a cylindrical lens between the laser and the sample. The beam is then focused on the sample over a length of 10 to 25 mm instead of a few microns. This "line focus" method can reduce power density per unit area as much as a factor of 1/1000.[*] Alternatively, the laser line may be chosen to fall within a region where there is no significant absorption by the sample.

We will now describe a number of more complicated techniques that have been successfully employed for the study of colored compounds.

Rotating Sample Techniques

Liquids

Figure 2.4. shows a cylindrical quartz cell designed by Kiefer and Bernstein.[+] This cell is symmetrically glued onto a circular piece of brass which has a central rod that fits into a chuck connected to a motor rotating from 0 to 3000 rpm. Although the cell has a volume of ~65 ml, only ~15 ml of liquid are necessary since the centrifugal force during rotation drives the liquid to the outer part of the cell. The laser beam must be focused to this area (near the wall) to minimize the absorption of Raman scattered light by the liquid itself (self-absorption). The focus of the laser beam must not fall on the glass wall since that will cause spurious lines originating within the glass to be observed. Figure 2.5 shows a similar liquid cell reported by Clark.[‡]

---

[*] H. H. Eysel and S. Sunder, Appl. Spectrosc., 34, 89 (1980).

[+] W. Kiefer and H. J. Bernstein, Appl. Spectrosc., 25, 500 (1971).

[‡] R. J. H. Clark, Spex Speaker, 18, 1, (1973).

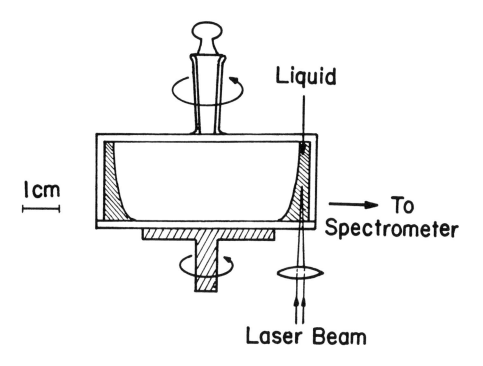

Figure 2.4. Rotating cylindrical cell (rotation below).

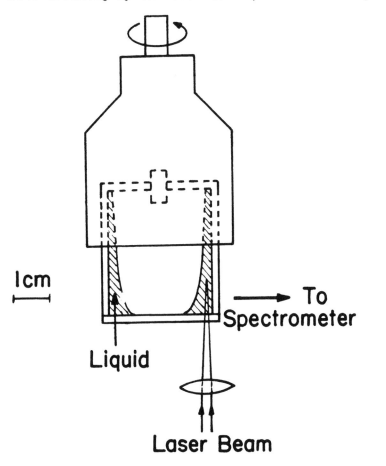

Figure 2.5. Rotating cylindrical cell (rotation above).

Since the laser beam is aimed at the bottom corner of these cells, it is necessary to use a cell with minimum distortion at the corners.

As stated earlier, the absorption of Raman scattered light by the solution itself is a serious problem in resonance Raman spectroscopy. According to Strekas et al., the following equation gives the optimum concentration to minimize self-absorption:[*]

$$A_{opt} = 1/(2kr) \qquad (1)$$

Here A_{opt} is the optimum absorbance of the solution, k is log (e) = 2.303, and r is the path length (cm) of the scattered radiation inside the cell. The equation was derived by assuming that r is equal to the path length to the point of scattering, within the cell. If r = 0.5 cm, A_{opt} = 0.434. This equation does not include the molecular extinction coefficient or the concentration of the solute in solution. Ard and Susi also confirmed the validity of this equation.[+]

Woodruff and Spiro developed another useful technique for resonance Raman studies of solution.[‡] In their method the solution is circulated through a capillary cell using a peristaltic pump, as shown in Figure 2.6.

[*] T. C. Strekas, D. H. Adams, A. Packer, and T. G. Spiro, Appl. Spectros., 28, 324 (1974).

[+] J. S. Ard and H. Susi, Appl. Spectrosc., 32, 321 (1978).

[‡] W. H. Woodruff and T. G. Spiro, Appl. Spectrosc., 28, 74 (1974).

By immersing a part of the circulating loop in a constant temperature bath,

it is possible to measure the spectrum over a wide range of temperatures.

Anderson and Kincaid developed a more sophisticated technique which allows

the measurements of redox potentials and electronic spectra as well as

Raman spectra using a circulating cell.[*]

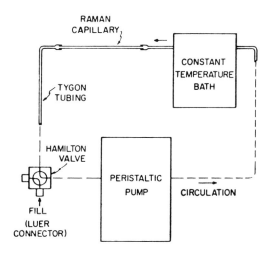

Figure 2.6. Flow-through system employing a peristaltic pump (reproduced by
         permission).

---

[*] J. L. Anderson and J. R. Kincaid, Appl. Spectrosc., 32, 356 (1978).

Solids

(Resonance) Raman spectra of solid samples can be measured by preparing pellets such as those described in Section 2.1 and rotating them using the motor depicted in Figure 2.7. Such a rotating device is

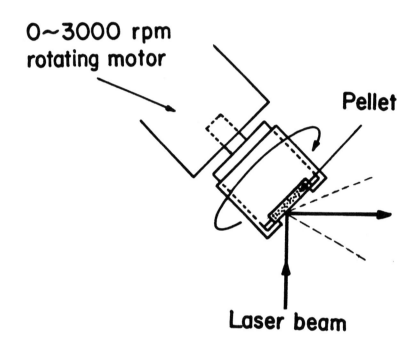

Figure 2.7. Sample rotation configuration for solid pellets.

commercially available from Raman instrument manufacturers. Kiefer and Bernstein designed a special die with a ring-shaped, grooved disk directly connected to the rotating shaft.[*] The sample is packed in the groove and thus requires much smaller amounts. By reducing the width of the groove to

* W. Kiefer and H. J. Bernstein, Appl. Spectrosc., 25, 609 (1971).

1 mm and placing the sample on top of a powdered KBr layer, Long et al. were able to measure the Raman spectra of samples as small as 1 mg.[*]

Gases

Although there has not been much work done in the area of strongly absorbing vapors, the description of a rotating cell for absorbing vapors at high temperatures is in the literature.[+]

Surface Scanning Techniques

In some cases it is desirable to rotate the sample and keep it cold at the same time. In doing so, we may scan the surface of the sample, which is kept at a fixed position on a cold tip, by oscillating the laser beam along one direction or rotating it on the sample. Koningstein and Gachter oscillate the laser beam linearly on the sample surface (Figure 2.8).[‡] Clark and Turtle[δ] employ a setup that permits the laser beam to be flicked rapidly on the sample surface which is held at liquid nitrogen temperature (Fig. 2.9).

---

[*] G. J. Long, L. J. Basile, and J. R. Ferraro, Appl. Spectrosc., 28, 73 (1974).

[+] R. J. H. Clark, O. H. Ellestad, and P. D. Mitchell, Applied Spectrosc., 28, 575 (1974).

[‡] J. A. Koningstein and B. F. Gachter, J. Opt. Soc. Am., 63, 892 (1973).

[δ] R. J. H. Clark and P. C. Turtle, Inorg. Chem., 17, 2526 (1978).

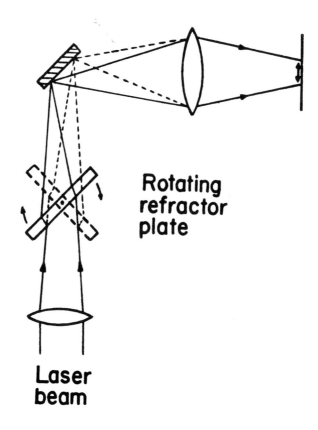

Rotating refractor plate

Laser beam

Figure 2.8. Oscillating beam sample configuration.

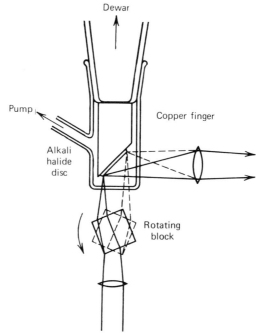

Dewar

Pump

Copper finger

Alkali halide disc

Rotating block

Figure 2.9. Low temperature oscillating beam sample configuration (reproduced by permission).

Zimmerer and Kiefer have also designed a rotating surface-scanning technique for a sample cooled by a cryostat.[*] Homborg and Preetz designed a cell that allows the measurement of Raman spectra of rotating samples at liquid nitrogen temperatures.[+]

2.3 DIFFERENCE SPECTROSCOPY

Raman difference spectroscopy is a useful technique for subtracting solvent bands from solution spectra and in determining small shifts of solute bands due to isotopic substitution or interaction with any other molecule. Kiefer designed a cylindrical cell which is divided into two equal parts similar to that shown in Figure 2.10; one containing the solution and the other containing only the solvent.[‡] By rotating such a cell, the laser

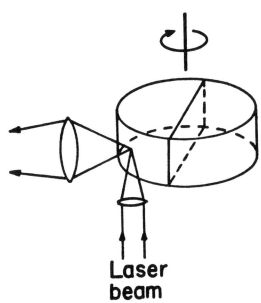

Laser beam

Figure 2.10. Split cell for Raman difference spectroscopy.

* N. Zimmerer and W. Kiefer, Appl. Spectrosc., 28, 279 (1974).

+ H. Homborg and W. Preetz, Spectrochim. Acta, 32A, 709 (1976).

‡ W. Kiefer, Appl. Spectrosc., 27, 253 (1973).

beam irradiates the solution and the solvent alternately. To record the difference spectrum, an electronic system containing a gated differential amplifier must be constructed. Later Kiefer et al.[*] designed a universal rotating system that can be used for (1) difference spectroscopy, (2) normal rotating sample techniques (solid and solution), and (3) automatic scanning of the depolarization ratios as a function of the wave number. Small isotope shifts observed by this method may be calculated as described by Laane.[+]

2.4. THERMOSTATED CELLS

In Raman studies of biological molecules such as proteins and nucleic acids, it is often necessary to heat a solution to a precise temperature and maintain that temperature during the measurement so that conformational changes are avoided. Such cells have been devised by Thomas and Barylski[‡], and Fox and Tu.[δ] In both cases, capillary tubing containing the sample is horizontally inserted into a metal (copper or brass) block whose temperature is controlled by circulating thermostated water[‡] or by a heating rod.[δ] The temperature of the solution is measured by a thermocouple placed within the cell[‡] or imbedded near the capillary.[δ] The former[‡] covers the range 5-95°C with ±0.25° C accuracy, whereas the latter[δ] covers the range from room temperature

---

* W. Kiefer, W. J. Schmid, and J. A. Topp, Appl. Spectrosc., 29, 434 (1975).
+ J. Laane, Appl. Spectrosc., 37, 474 (1983).
‡ G. J. Thomas, Jr., and J. R. Barylski, Appl. Spectrosc., 24, 463 (1970).
δ J. W. Fox and A. T. Tu, Appl. Spectrosc., 33, 647 (1979).

to +100°C with ±1°C accuracy. A circulating solution cell which can be thermostated is depicted in Figure 2.6.

2.5. HIGH TEMPERATURE CELLS

A simple furnace for obtaining Raman spectra of fused salts (up to 500°C) was designed by Begun and is shown in Figure 2.11.[*] The sample is sealed in a small glass or quartz tube under vacuum, and then the tube is wrapped by nichrome or platinum wire. The furnace (made of a hydrous aluminum silicate) is rectangular, as shown in the figure.

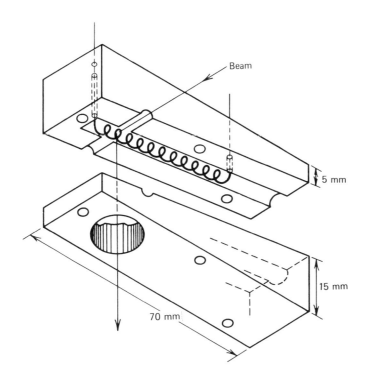

Figure 2.11. High temperature cell (<500°C) (reproduced by permission).

---

* G. M. Begun, Appl. Spectrosc., 26, 400 (1972).

For metal salts which melt at higher temperatures (up to 1000°C), such as NaBF$_4$ and Na$_3$AlF$_6$, two types of Raman cells are available; one is a windowless cell in which the liquid is retained by its surface tension[*], and the other is a graphite cell with diamond windows.[+]

2.6. LOW TEMPERATURE CELLS

A very simple device that may be used to obtain Raman spectra at liquid nitrogen temperature has been reported by Miller and Harney.[‡] As is shown in Figure 2.12, the sample (liquid or particles) is contained in a thin-walled

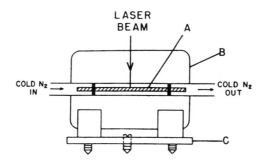

Figure 2.12. Variable temperature cell: A, sample tube; B, evacuated annular jacket for insulation; C, metal support (reproduced by permission.)

---

[*] A. S. Quist, Appl. Spectrosc., 25, 80 (1971); B. Gilbert, G. Momantov, and G. M. Begun, Appl. Spectrosc., 29, 276 (1975).

[+] S. K. Ratkje and E. Rytter, J. Phys. Chem., 78, 1449 (1974).

[‡] F. A. Miller and B. M. Harney, Appl. Spectrosc., 24, 291 (1970).

melting point tube, which is placed in the center of an evacuated annular jacket, and cold nitrogen gas is passed through the center of the jacket. Any temperature down to -150°C can be achieved easily. The temperature is measured with a thermocouple placed near the sample. This device is also used for obtaining Raman spectra at high temperatures by using hot air instead of cold nitrogen. According to these authors, temperatures in excess of 200°C can be obtained with a heat gun and a cone of aluminum foil to direct the flow of air. Low temperature cells with rotating devices have already been mentioned in Section 2.2.

Simple Dewar cells such as the one shown in Figure 2.13 may also be used for measuring Raman spectra of liquids at low temperatures. The laser beam enters vertically from the bottom, and the scattered light is observed from the horizontal direction, as shown in the figure. Since the laser beam is aimed at a bottom corner of the cell, the bottom part of the cell must be made optically flat to minimize distortion. Obviously this part of the cell is not silvered. The central tube has a standard joint on one end so that transfer of a liquid from the container to the cell can be made using standard vacuum techniques. Liquid nitrogen and organic slushes are used as coolants.

In our laboratory a "mini-bulb" method was developed to obtain Raman spectra of liquids at low temperatures.[*] As shown in Figure 2.14, the sample

---

[*] K. Nakamoto, Y. Nonaka, T. Ishiguro, M. W. Urban, M. Suzuki, M. Kozuka, Y. Nishida, and S. Kida, J. Am. Chem. Soc., 104, 3386 (1982).

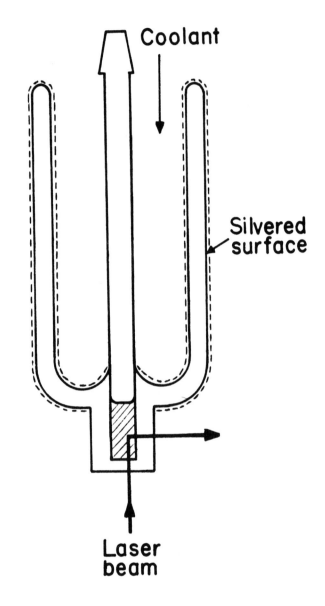

Figure 2.13. Simple Dewar cell for low temperature Raman spectroscopy.

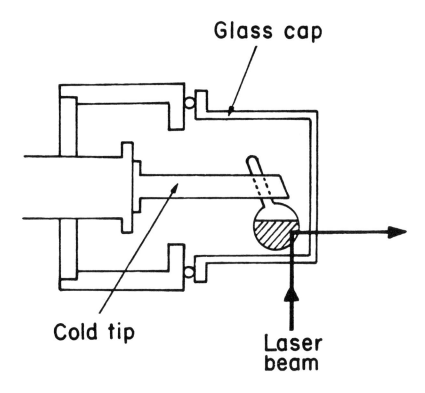

Glass cap

Cold tip

Laser beam

Figure 2.14. Raman mini-bulb configuration.

solution is contained in a small bulb (0.4 ml) which is attached to the front edge of a cold tip cooled by a closed-cycle helium refrigerator. Any temperature between -80°C and room temperature can be obtained by controlling the temperature of the cryocooler. Temperature measurement within the sample is not easily done using thermocouples. One method involves the calculation of temperature from the intensity ratios of the Stokes and anti-Stokes Raman lines, using the following formula:

$$\frac{I\text{ (Stokes)}}{I\text{ (anti-Stokes)}} = \frac{(\tilde{\nu}_o - \tilde{\nu}_k)^4}{(\tilde{\nu}_o + \tilde{\nu}_k)^4} \exp\{hc\tilde{\nu}_k/kT\} \tag{1}$$

where $\tilde{\nu}_o$ is the wave number of the laser line, $\tilde{\nu}_k$, the wave number of a band of the sample, h, Planck's constant, c, the velocity of light, k, Boltzmann's constant, and T, absolute temperature.   A more convenient equation may be written as

$$T = \frac{-\tilde{\nu}_k \times 1.43879}{\left[\ln \dfrac{I\text{ (anti-Stokes)}}{I\text{ (Stokes)}} + 4 \ln \dfrac{\tilde{\nu}_o - \tilde{\nu}_k}{\tilde{\nu}_o + \tilde{\nu}_k}\right]} \tag{2}$$

A problem that is frequently encountered when employing these techniques is the appearance of a broad, ill-defined envelope between 500 and 200 cm^{-1} which is due to Raman scattering from the glass or quartz. This envelope may be eliminated by the use of the low temperature cell depicted in Figure 2.15. In this method the Raman scattering originates directly from the surface of a frozen solution. Details of the operation of this cell are given in the original paper.[*]

---

[*] R. S. Czernuszewicz and M. K. Johnson, Appl. Spectrosc., 37, 297 (1983).

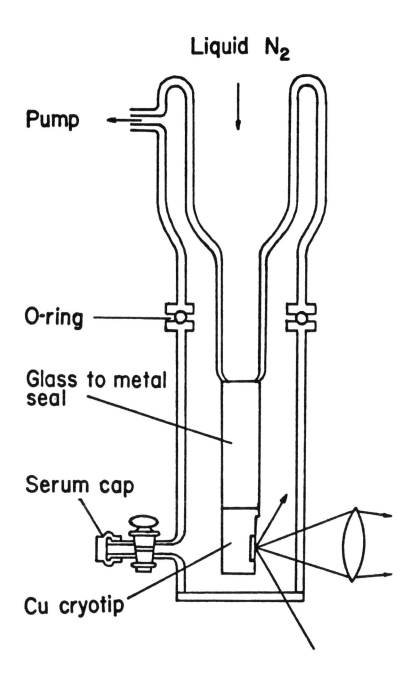

Liquid N$_2$

Pump

O-ring

Glass to metal
seal

Serum cap

Cu cryotip

Figure 2.15. Low temperature cell for frozen solutions.

2.7. 180 DEGREE (BACKSCATTERING) GEOMETRY

Although 90 degree scattering geometry is the most commonly used, the 180 degree (backscattering) geometry described in this section and depicted in Figure 1.6 has several advantages over the former. Figure 2.16 shows the apparatus designed by Shriver and Dunn.[*] It is a simple and versatile design that allows the rotation and cooling of the sample simultaneously. Also sample placement and focusing of the laser beam on absorbing samples can be done easily and quickly.

As stated in Section 2.3, there is an optimum concentration which is required to maximize the Raman signal for 90 degree scattering. This is not true for backscattering geometry which has a plateau in the curve of Raman scattering as opposed to concentration. Other advantages include (1) ease of correction for self-absorption in highly colored solutions, (2) the ability to measure Raman scattering and UV-visible absorption in the same cell,[+] (3) the ability to obtain single crystal Raman spectra on small crystals with only one good face for each orientation, whereas two are required for 90 degree scattering, and (4) the ability to obtain low temperature spectra of

---

* D. F. Shriver and J. B. R. Dunn, Appl. Spectrosc., 28, 319, (1974).

+ E. G. Rodgers and D. P. Strommen, Appl. Spectrosc., 35, 215 (1981).

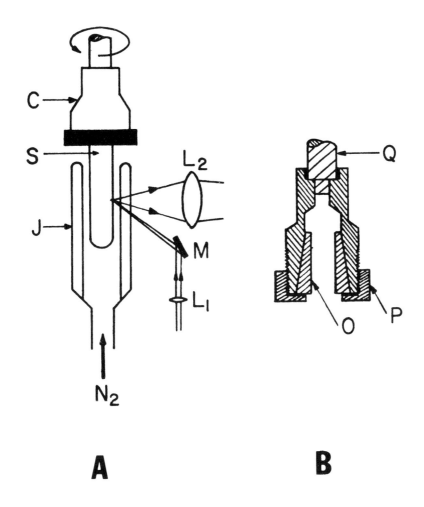

A   **B**

Figure 2.16. Sample spinner for 180 degree (or oblique) illumination:
(a) Complete system with evacuated Pyrex jacket, J, surrounding
the sample tube, S; cold (or warm) gas such as N_2 is passed
through J to control the sample temperature. L_1, L_2, and M are
lenses and a mirror; C is the sample chuck. (b) Details of the
sample chuck; O, split nylon cone; P, knurled aluminum nut
attached to aluminum body of chuck; Q, spinner shaft. The
spinner should be constructed to minimize wobble of the sample
tube, which decreases the Raman signal at high absorber
concentrations. Reproduced by permission.

very small samples (see Figure 2.17).[*] There are of course some disadvantages, such as the appearance of the spurious background due to various glasses (see Section 2.2) and the danger of specular reflection of the laser beam into the monochromator. The intensity of the former may be minimized by using lenses with short depths of focus.

2.8. SPECIAL TECHNIQUES

There are numerous other highly specialized techniques that allow Raman spectra to be obtained from a variety of situations. The conditions under which Raman spectra can be obtained are limited only by the ingenuity of the researcher. Clearly we cannot present detailed descriptions in this book of all approaches. However, there are a few techniques that need brief mention.

Raman Microprobe—It is possible to obtain spectra from surface regions of only a few microns in diameter by using microscope objectives in the sampling scheme. Commercial instruments that accomplish this are available from Spex Industries (Micramate) and Instruments S.A. (MOLE), and the literature fairly abounds with applications.[+] Apparently the major drawback of this approach is the local heating problem.

---

[*] B. M. Sjöberg, T. M. Loehr, and J. Sanders-Loehr, Biochem., 21, 96 (1982).

[+] G. J. Rosasco, "Raman Microprobe Spectroscopy", in Advances in Infrared and Raman Spectroscopy, Vol. 7, R. J. H. Clark and R. E. Hester, eds. (Heyden, London, 1980).

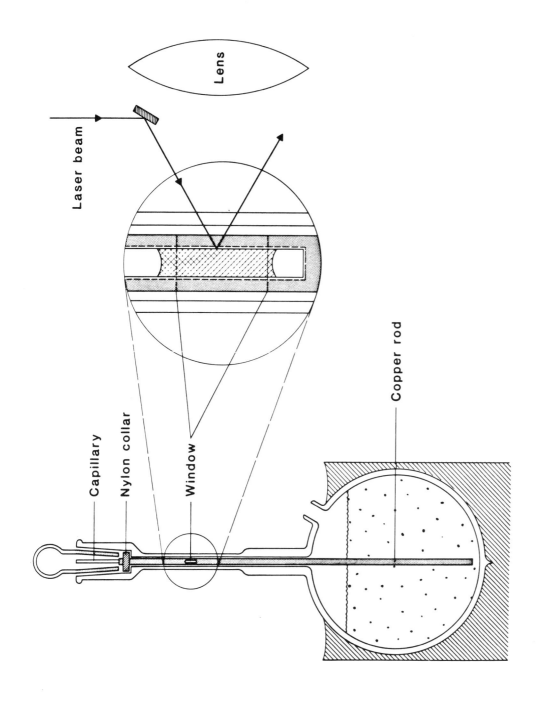

Figure 2.17. Dewar and cold-finger sample holder (reproduced by permission).

Laser beam

Lens

Capillary

Nylon collar

Window

Copper rod

Spectroelectrochemistry—Jeanmaire et al. pioneered in the use of Raman to study the surfaces of electrochemical cells.[*] They were able to obtain RR spectra of electrogenerated intermediates and products from or near the electrode surfaces. Two types of cells have been designed: a controlled potential electrolysis cell to study the bulk solution and a "sandwich" cell to study the surface species.

High Pressure Spectroscopy—Raman spectra obtained under high pressure often provide valuable information about intermolecular interaction, phase transition, structure change, and vibrational assignments and so forth. Basically two types of high pressure Raman cells are available. One is the diamond anvil cell, and the other is the piston-cylinder-type cell. Both types are reviewed by Ferraro and Basile and improved versions of the former are described by Adams et al.[+] Using these cells, it is possible to measure Raman spectra of solids and liquids up to 200 Kbars.

---

[*] D. L. Jeanmaire, M. R. Suchanski, and R. P. Van Duyne, J. Am. Chem. Soc., 97, 1699 (1975).

[+] J. R. Ferraro and L. J. Basile, Appl. Spectrosc., 28, 505 (1974); D. M. Adams, S. J. Payne, and K. Martin, Appl. Spectrosc., 27, 377 (1973).

Matrix Isolation Spectroscopy—If it is desirable to obtain Raman spectra of isolated molecules or unstable species, one can isolate them in inert gas matrices using the matrix isolation technique. This is done in the same fashion as for IR experiments,[*] with the added complications that rigorously clear matrices are required and fluorescence due to the diffusion pump oil can be problematic. The optimum conditions for obtaining good samples may be found in the article by Barnes et al. and a rather clever oven that employs the laser as a heating source to vaporize the sample is described by Scheuermann and Nakamoto.[+]

---

[*] M. Moskovits and G. A. Ozin, Cryochemistry, (Wiley, New York, 1976).

[+] A. J. Barnes, J. C. Bignall, and C. J. Purnell, J. Raman Spectrosc., 4, 159 (1975); W. Scheuermann and K. Nakamoto, Appl. Spectrosc., 32, 251 (1978).

CHAPTER 3. INSTRUMENT CALIBRATION

3.1. FREQUENCY CALIBRATION

Raman spectrophotometers are no different from any other spectral device. That is to say, the wave number or wavelength readings on the machine are not to be trusted. We recommend that the instrument be calibrated at the time any spectrum is taken. The time involved in calibration will depend on the accuracy desired for a particular experiment. Raman spectrophotometers are typically calibrated for frequency by one of four different methods. These are the use of internal standards, indene, laser plasma lines, and the Ne emission spectrum. In this section we will briefly discuss each of these.

Internal Standards

Where accuracy of no greater than 1 cm^{-1} is required, internal standards may be employed. These may consist of solvent bands or the bands of added noninteracting solutes. In Chapter 5 we will present the Raman spectra and some of the frequencies of commonly used solvents as well as frequencies associated with useful water-soluble species. Bands due to the compounds under consideration may be measured relative to the positions of these internal standard bands. However, care must be taken when using this approach since significant band shifts may occur through chemical interaction between the reference and the substance under study. In addition to its inherent simplicity this method has a distinct advantage over the remaining three in that the absolute readings from the monochromator may change from day to day by as much as 2 to 3 cm^{-1} if the temperature control inside the monochromator happens to malfunction, whereas frequencies determined from the position of a band relative to an internal standard are essentially temperature independent.

Indene

If accuracy on the order of 0.5 cm^{-1} is desired, then indene may be used. Indene has long been used as a frequency calibrant for IR spectrophotometers and it has been shown by Hendra and Loader that it also may be used for routine calibration of Raman spectrophotometers.[*] Before using indene as a calibrant, it should be vacuum distilled and stored in a sealed capillary or a NMR tube. A reproduction of a spectrum taken in this laboratory is shown in Chapter 5 (Figure 5.6a). Table 3.1 is a compilation of frequencies that are recommended for use in calibration. The frequencies are numbered according to the spectrum shown in Chapter 5. Clearly indene will not be a good choice if the bands under study are between 1700 and 2700 cm^{-1}. A more extensive list of the frequencies may be found in the paper by Hendra and Loader.[*]

---

[*] P. J. Hendra and E. J. Loader, Chem. Ind., 718 (1968).

Table 3.1. Recommended Frequencies from the Spectrum of Indene

Band[a]	Wave Number (cm^{-1})
1	730.4 ± 0.5
2	1018.3 ± 0.5
3	1205.6 ± 0.5
4	1552.7 ± 0.5
5	1610.2 ± 0.5
6	2892.2 ± 1
7	3054.7 ± 1

a. The numbers refer to Figure 5.6a.

Laser Plasma Lines

The principal plasma lines of the Ar-ion laser which may be used for calibration are tabulated in Table 3.2, and the corresponding spectrum is shown in Figure 1.3. These lines can be obtained by detuning the laser and collecting the scattered radiation from a Kimax melting point tube as suggested by Craig and Levin.[*] This method gives a calibration better than 1 cm^{-1} accuracy.

Ne Emission Lines

If a neon lamp is available, the Ne emission lines may be used to obtain a high degree of accuracy in frequency calibration over a wide range of frequencies. We have employed a simple neon lamp which can be purchased from a commercial electronic shop. Figure 3.1 (a and b) give a spectrum of such a Ne lamp which was taken on our system. Tables 3.3 and 3.4 list the Ne frequencies which may be used for calibration when obtaining spectra with a He-Ne and an Ar-ion laser, respectively. The Ne lamp is of limited use at energies higher than 17,500 cm^{-1} where most of the data will be taken if an Ar-ion laser is employed.

A rather interesting method for calibrating cosecant drive monochromators that requires only three known frequencies has been outlined by Bergström et al.[+]

---

[*] N. C. Craig and I. W. Levin, Appl. Spectrosc., 33, 475 (1979).
[+] G. Bergström, S. Forss, and F. Stenman, J. Raman Spectrosc., 9, 403 (1980).

Table 3.2. Some Plasma Lines from a Detuned Argon Ion Laser

Line	Wavelength in Air (Å)	Wave Number in Air (cm^{-1})	Reference
1	4545.05	22,001.96	a
2	4579.35	21,837.16	a
3	4589.93	21,786.82	b
4	4609.56	21,694.04	a
5	?	?	—
6	4657.89	21,468.95	a
7	4726.86	21,155.69	a
8	4735.93	21,115.18	b
9	4764.89	20,986.84	b
10	4806.07	20,807.02	b
11	4847.90	20,627.49	b
12	4879.86	20,492.39	c
13	4889.03	20,453.96	c
14	4904.75	20,388.40	c
15	4933.21	20,270.78	c
16	4965.07	20,140.70	c
17	4972.16	20,111.98	c
18	5009.33	19,962.75	c
19	5017.16	19,931.59	c
20	5062.04	19,754.88	c
21	5141.79	19,448.48	c
22	5145.32	19,435.14	c

a. R. Beck, W. Englisch, and K. Gurs, Tables of Laser Lines in Gases and Vapors, 2d ed., (Springer-Verlag, New York, 1978) pp. 4-5.

b. A. N. Zaidel, V. K. Prokofev, and S. M. Raiskii, Tables of Spectrum Lines (Pergamon Press, New York, 1961) pp. 299-301.

c. N. C. Craig and I. W. Levin, Appl. Spectrosc., 33, 475 (1979).

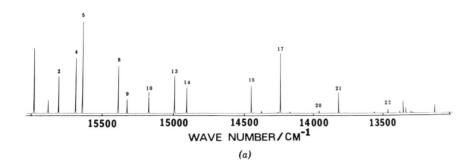

Figure 3.1. Ne lamp spectrum: (a) Band numbers refer to Table 3.3;

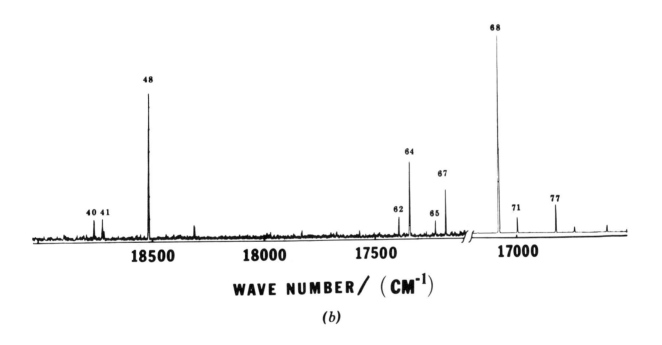

(b) band numbers refer to Table 3.4.

Table 3.3. Calibration Lines of a Ne Lamp that Are Useful for He-Ne Excitation

Line	Wavelength in Air (Å)[a]	Wave Number in Air (cm^{-1})
1	6328.1646	15,802.3702
2	6334.4279	15,786.7453
3	6351.8618	15,743.4156
4	6382.9914	15,666.6356
5	6402.2460	15,619.5185
6	6421.7108	15,572.1743
7	6444.7118	15,516.5977
8	6506.5279	15,369.1802
9	6532.8824	15,307.179
10	6598.9529	15,153.9193
11	6652.0925	15,032.8637
12	6666.8967	14.999.4824
13	6678.2764	14,973.9235
14	6717.0428	14,887.5038
15	6929.4672	14,431.1239
16	7024.0500	14,236.8007
17	7032.4128	14,219.8706
18	7051.2937	14,181.7948
19	7059.1079	14,166.096
20	7173.9380	13,939.3455
21	7245.1665	13,802.3053
22	7438.8981	13,442.8512
23	7472.4383	13,382.5126
24	7488.8712	13,353.1473
25	7535.7739	13,270.0372
26	7544.0439	13,255.4902
27	7724.6281	12,945.6071
28	7839.0550	12,756.6397
29	7927.1172	12,614.9264
30	7936.9946	12,599.2274
31	7943.1805	12,589.4155
32	8082.4576	12,372.4744
33	8118.5495	12,317.4712
34	8128.9077	12,301.7758
35	8136.4061	12,290.4387
36	8248.6812	12,123.1501
37	8259.3795	12,107.4471
38	8266.0788	12,097.6345
39	8267.1166	12,096.1158

a. K. Burns, K. B. Adams, and J. Longwell, J. Opt. Soc. Am., 40, 339 (1950)

Table 3.4. Calibration Lines of a Ne Lamp that Are Useful for Argon Ion
Excitation

Line	Wavelength in Air (Å)[a]	Wave Number in Air (cm^{-1})
1	4884.9170	20,471.1769
2	4892.1007	20,441.1164
3	4928.241	20,291.2155
4	4939.0457	20,246.8262
5	4944.9899	20,222.4882
6	4957.0355	20,173.3476
7	4957.123	20,172.9915
8	4994.913	20,020.3687
9	5005.1587	19,979.3865
10	5011.	19,956.0966
11	5022.864	19,908.9603
12	5031.3504	19,875.3798
13	5037.7512	19,850.1268
14	5074.2007	19,707.5374
15	5080.3852	19,683.5468
16	5104.7011	19,589.7856
17	5113.6724	19,555.4178
18	5116.5032	19,544.5984
19	5122.2565	19,522.6459
20	5144.9384	19,436.5787
21	5151.9610	19,410.0848
22	5154.4271	19,400.7982
23	5156.6672	19,392.3703
24	5158.9018	19,383.9705
25	5188.6122	19,272.9763
26	5191.3223	19,262.915
27	5193.1302	19,256.2089
28	5193.2227	19,255.8659
29	5203.8962	19,216.371
30	5208.8648	19,198.041
31	5210.5672	19,191.7686
32	5214.3389	19,177.8866
33	5222.3517	19,148.4614
34	5234.0271	19,105.7475
35	5274.0393	18,960.7992
36	5280.0853	18,939.088
37	5298.1891	18,874.3735
38	5304.7580	18,851.0013
39	5326.3968	18,774.418
40	5330.7775	18,758.9897
41	5341.0938	18,722.7567

Table 3.4. Continued

Line	Wavelength in Air (Å)[a]	Wave Number in Air (cm^{-1})
42	5343.2834	18,715.0844
43	5349.2038	18,694.3709
44	5360.0121	18,656.6743
45	5372.3110	18,613.9633
46	5374.9774	18,604.7294
47	5383.2503	18,576.1379
48	5400.5616	18,516.5928
49	5412.6490	18,475.2420
50	5418.5584	18,455.0931
51	5433.6513	18,403.831
52	5448.5091	18,353.6447
53	5494.4158	18,200.2971
54	5533.6788	18,071.1609
55	5538.6510	18,054.9379
56	5562.7662	17,976.6678
57	5652.5664	17,691.0792
58	5656.6588	17,678.2803
59	5662.5489	17,659.8916
60	5689.8163	17,575.2599
61	5719.2248	17,484.8871
62	5748.2985	17,396.4522
63	5760.5885	17,359.3375
64	5764.4188	17,347.8027
65	5804.4496	17,228.1623
66	5811.4066	17,207.538
67	5820.1558	17,181.6706
68	5852.4878	17,086.7507
69	5868.4183	17,040.3667
70	5872.8275	17,027.5732
71	5881.8950	17,001.3235
72	5902.9623	16,942.082
73	5902.7835	16,941.16
74	5906.4294	16,930.7027
75	5913.6327	16,910.0797
76	5918.9068	16,895.0118
77	5944.8342	16,821.327
78	5961.6228	16,773.9562
79	5965.4710	16,763.1357
80	5974.6273	16,737.4457
81	5975.5340	16,734.906
82	5987.9074	16,700.3251
83	5991.6532	16,689.8845
84	6000.9275	16,664.0907
85	6029.9971	16,583.7559
86	6046.1348	16,539.4923
87	6064.5359	16,489.3079

a. K. Burns, K. B. Adams, and J. Longwell, J. Opt. Soc. Am., 40, 339 (1950).

3.2. INTENSITY CALIBRATION

In order to use Raman spectroscopy as a quantitative tool, the intensity
of the Raman lines must be measured. Depending on the application, peak
height, peak height times half-width, or mechanical integration may be used
to obtain a parameter related to the absolute (integrated) intensity of a
band. Unfortunately the intensity of a Raman line is controlled by a number
of factors, including incident laser power, frequency of the scattered radiation, absorptivity of the materials involved in the scattering, and the
response of the detection system. The situation is further complicated by
the fact that many of these parameters are dependent on frequency as
indicated in the following equation:

$$I = K(\nu) \times A(\nu) \times \nu^4 \times I_o \times J(\nu) \times C \qquad (1)$$

where I is the intensity of a Raman line, $K(\nu)$ describes the overall spectrophotometer response, $A(\nu)$ is the self-absorption of the medium, ν the frequency
of the scattered radiation, I_o the intensity of the incident radiation, $J(\nu)$
a molar scattering parameter, and C the concentration of the scattering
species.

Raman spectra may be conveniently used to determine the amount of a
material in a solution if the particular material under study shows at least
one Raman band of reasonable intensity. In general, relative rather than
absolute Raman intensities are employed. A working curve must first be
prepared from the spectra of a series of solutions that contain varying
amounts of the material under consideration and a constant amount of a
noninteracting species. For aqueous solutions, ClO_4^- is a convenient choice

because it is chemically inert and has a strong Raman band at 928 cm^{-1}. Other possibilities are listed in Chapter 5. Then a relative intensity is calculated for each solution by dividing the intensity of the strongest band of the material whose concentration is being determined by that of the internal standard. Thus a relative intensity of the following form is obtained.

$$I_{rel} = \frac{K(\nu) \times A(\nu) \times \nu^4 \times J(\nu) \times C}{K(\nu') \times A(\nu') \times (\nu')^4 \times J(\nu') \times C_{IS}} \qquad (2)$$

where all the terms involving ν' indicate those of the internal standard, and C and C_{IS} denote the concentrations of the solution being investigated and the internal standard, respectively. Although the lead terms do not cancel, they remain constant, and the resulting equation is of the form:

$$I_{rel} = \text{constant} \times C \qquad (3)$$

Thus a standard working curve may be prepared and employed as in any other quantitative technique.

Excitation profiles (Raman intensity as a function of the exciting laser wavelength) which are used in resonance Raman studies are similar in nature to those obtained from fluorescence experiments and yield important data regarding excited electronic states (electronic transitions) as well as molecular symmetry. When constructing excitation proviles, it is the frequency dependence of $J(\nu)$ that is of interest. However, it is somewhat more difficult to ascertain the J dependence on ν from intensity changes since K and A also vary with ν. Thus it is necessary to eliminate all of these other frequency-dependent parameters. The ν^4 dependence of the intensity can

readily be taken into account; however, the self-absorption and spectrophotometer corrections are more involved.

Iganaki et al. have shown that self-absorption can be accounted for by
incorporation of the expression

$$\frac{A(\nu)}{A(\nu')} = \frac{\varepsilon(\nu')}{\varepsilon(\nu)} \cdot \frac{1 - \exp(-\varepsilon(\nu)C \times 1}{1 - \exp(-\varepsilon(\nu')C \times 1} \qquad (4)$$

where $\varepsilon(\nu)$ is the molar absorptivity at ν , C the concentration of the
absorber and 1 the path length.[*]

The correction for the spectrophotometer response is somewhat more complicated. It is possible to make this correction using standard light sources
obtainable from the National Bureau of Standards; however, we have used the
following alternative method. First, obtain a tungsten lamp and an
appropriately regulated power supply. The lamp is then mounted in place of
the sample in front of the collection lens. The lamp is turned on, and after
about 15 minutes the temperature of the filament is measured with an optical
pyrometer. The signal of this lamp is then recorded over all desired wavelengths. We recommend that the temperature of the filament be frequently
checked throughout the spectral acquisition time. Next the observed signal
and the frequency results are compared to those predicted from Planck's law:

$$E(\nu)d\nu = \frac{8\pi h\nu^3}{c^3} \frac{d\nu}{e^{h\nu/kT} -1} \qquad (5)$$

where $E(\nu)\,d\nu$ is the energy per unit volume, h Planck's constant,   the
frequency, k Boltzmann's constant, T the absolute temperature, and c the

---

* F. Inagaki, M. Tasumi, and T. Miyazawa, J. Mol. Spectrosc., 50, 286 (1974).

velocity of light. According to Equation (5), the intensity depends only on the temperature of the blackbody radiator and the frequency of the emitted radiation. Thus the temperature is inserted into Equation (5) and its values are calculated at various frequencies and scaled to the experimental maximum. The calculated values are then overlayed on the experimental data, and the correction factor is obtained. Figure 3.2 shows a sensitivity curve obtained for our system. The reader of course should not use this curve for any other system. Corrections to intensities may then be made by hand, or the data may be digitized and corrected by a computer. If the data are collected directly into a computer, the correction will appear on the hard copies of the spectra. If higher accuracy is desired, we refer to the method proposed by Perkampus et al.[*] However, in both of these procedures, the temperature of the portion of the tungsten filament focused on the detector may not be accurately known. Alternative procedures are available that overcome this difficulty.[+]

---

[*] H. H. Perkampus, K. Kortüm, and H. Bruns, Appl. Spectrosc., 23, 105 (1969).

[+] M. D'Orazio and B. Schrader, J. Raman Spectrosc., 2, 585 (1974).

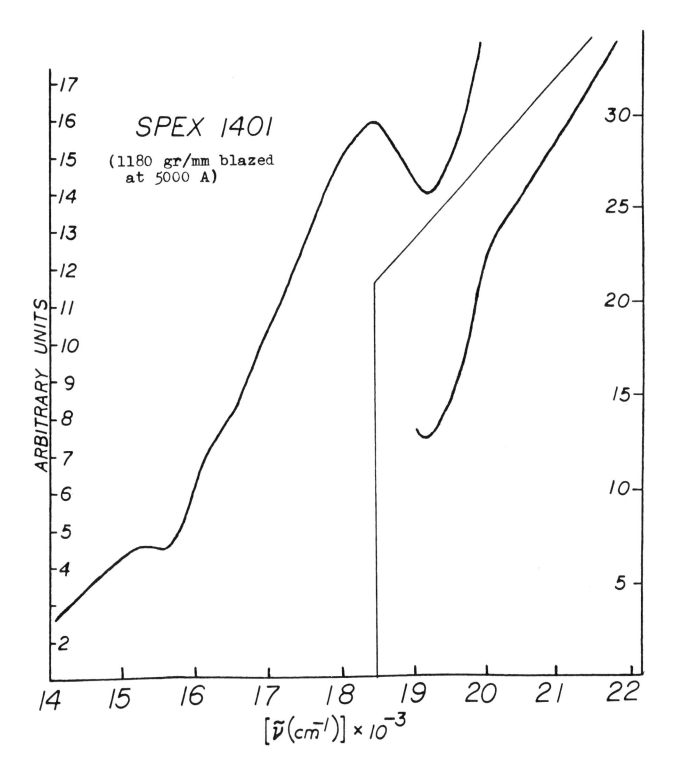

Figure 3.2. Sensitivity curve for a Spex Model 1401 double monochromator equipped with a RCA 3134A photomultiplier tube.

CHAPTER 4. OBTAINING RAMAN SPECTRA

The material in this chapter is intended to aid an experimentalist in obtaining a meaningful Raman spectrum. We will assume no prior knowledge of the instrument or its accessories. The chapter is divided into four parts: Instrument Start-up/Shut down Procedure, Data Collection, Depolarization Ratios, and Miscellaneous Problems. Some of the instructions will necessarily relate to our particular instrument; however we have left blank space wherever possible to allow readers to insert their specific parameters and locations.

4.1. INSTRUMENT START-UP/SHUT-DOWN PROCEDURE

Start-up for Gas Laser

Step 1: Turn on water supply to the laser (water light on).

Location:

Step 2: Turn on laser line switch (up).

Location:

Step 3: When "Ready" light comes on, push start button.

Location:

Step 4: Turn field control (on power supply) for highest output power reading. If buzzer sounds in first 15 minutes, turn down just until buzzing stops. If buzzer sounds after 15 minutes, check the pressure of the tube. Fill if necessary.

Location:

Step 5: Wait approximately 30 minutes for laser stabilization.

Start-up for Monochromator and Detection Electronics

Photon-Counting Method

Step 1:   Check to see that water is flowing through the photomultiplier cooling unit.

Location:

Step 2:   Turn on Main Power and Power switches.

Location:

Step 3:   Make sure power switch to photomultiplier cooler is on.

Location:

Step 4:   MAKE SURE SLITS ARE CLOSED!

Step 5:   Set High Voltage (HV) to _____; turn switch to On (Up).

Location:

Step 6:   Turn Digital Photometer to standby.

Location:

Step 7:   The initial settings on the photometer should be:

a. Trunc:

b. Lin:

c. Integration time: 100 counts

d. Mode: PC

e. Full scale: 50 K (50,000 counts/sec)

f. Zero Suppression: Off

Step 8:   The switch on the preamplifier should be set to PC output.

Location:

Step 9:   Detection mode switch should be set to PC output.

Location:

Step 10: <u>DO NOT USE PHOTOMULTIPLIER OVER _____ counts/sec OR PHOTOTUBE MAY BE DESTROYED.</u>

[Note: These instructions are designed for use with a Spex Digital Photometer and a Keithley 4145 picoammeter. The unit also has a circuitry for convenient interchange of the system (see Instructions A9 and B5). Before proceeding, read the manuals particular to your instrument.]

<u>Direct Current Method</u>

Step 1:   Check to see that water is flowing through the photomultiplier cooling unit.

<u>Location:</u>

Step 2.   Turn on Main Power and Power switches.

<u>Location:</u>

Step 3:   Make sure power switch to photomultiplier cooler is on.

<u>Location:</u>

Step 4:   <u>MAKE SURE SLITS ARE CLOSED.</u>

<u>Location:</u>

Step 5:   Turn the preamplifier to DC output.

<u>Location:</u>

Step 6:   Set High Voltage (HV) to _____; turn switch to On (Up).

<u>Location:</u>

Step 7:   Turn the picoammeter to (-).

<u>Location:</u>

Step 8.   Settings on picoammeter should be:

a. Rise time: N

b. Range: 0.1×10^{-6} A

c. Zero Suppression: Off

Step 9: Detection mode switch should be set at DC.

Step 10: <u>DO NOT USE AT CURRENT ABOVE THE _____ RANGE OR</u>

<u>PHOTOTUBE MAY BE DESTROYED.</u>

Shutdown for Gas Laser

Step 1: Turn the current down to minimum value.

Step 2: Turn line switch to Off.

Step 3: After 15 minutes shut off water supply to laser.

Shutdown for Monochromator and Detection Electronics

Photon-Counting Method

Step 1: <u>CLOSE THE SLITS!</u>

Step 2: Turn Photometer to Off; return all settings to those in
Step 7 of laser start-up procedure.

Step 3: Turn HV to Off.

Step 4: Turn off Main Power and Power switches.

Direct Current Method

Step 1: CLOSE THE SLITS!

Step 2: Turn the picoammeter to Off; return all settings to those
in Step 8 in monochromator and detection electronics.

Step 3: Turn HV to Off.

Step 4: Turn off Main Power and Power switches.

4.2. DATA COLLECTION

In Section 3.2 we discussed the use of internal standards in quantifying Raman intensities. We now consider the intensity of a non-resonant Raman signal of a compound at a given concentration using Equation (1) of Chapter 3. Then $A(\nu)$ is unity and $J(\nu)$ and C are constant. Thus, the Raman intensity is proportional only to $K(\nu) \times \nu^4 \times I_0$. Since $K(\nu)$ is itself a function of PM quantum efficiency, grating efficiency, and band pass used, the Raman intensity is determined by a total of five parameters. Using the 632.8 nm line of a He-Ne laser as the standard, Table 4.1 compares relative intensities obtained by using other laser lines under the conditions listed in the footnotes. It is seen, for example, that the Raman intensity of a band displaced by 3000 cm^{-1} from the Rayleigh line will be 86 times stronger with the 488.0 nm line of an Ar-ion laser than with the 632.8 nm line of a He-Ne laser. In the early days of laser Raman spectroscopy it was this intensity discrepancy that led to the misconception that C-H stretching modes were unusally weak Raman scatters. Among the lines listed in Table 4.1, the 488.0 nm line is clearly most advantageous in measuring nonresonant Raman bands.

The basic observables obtained from a Raman Spectrum are signal (S), signal-to-noise (S/N), and resolution or band pass (BP). These observables are related to one another by a set of independent parameters consisting of laser power (I_0), mechanical slit width (W), scan speed (R), time constant (T), and amplification factor or gain (G). The interrelationships among the observables are sometimes referred to as the "trading rules." For example, the resolution may be increased by decreasing the mechanical slit width since $BP \propto W$.

Table 4.1. Comparison of Different Laser Excitation Frequencies

Raman Region (cm⁻¹)	A Molecular Scattering Efficiency (ν^4 law)	B Relative Laser Power (80mW=1.0) (I_o)	C PM Quantum Efficiency[a]	D Grating Efficiency[b] $K(\nu)$	E Normalizing Factor for Equivalent Band Pass[c]	F Raman Intensity[d]
He-Ne Laser						
0 (6328 Å)	1.0	1.0	1.0	1.0	1.0	1.0
3000 (7811 Å)			0.5	0.80	1.6	0.64
Ar⁺ Laser						
0 (4880 Å)	2.8	14.0	3.1	1.2	0.59	86.
3000 (5717 Å)			1.4	1.1	0.81	49.
0 (5145 Å)	2.3	13.	2.5	1.2	0.65	58.
3000 (6084 Å)			1.0	1.1	0.91	30.
Kr⁺ Laser						
0 (5682 Å)	1.5	3.0	1.4	1.1	0.80	5.5
3000 (6850 Å)			0.80	1.0	1.1	4.0
0 (6471 Å)	0.90	5.0	1.0	1.0	1.0	4.5
3000 (8030 Å)			0.44	0.75	1.7	2.5

Note: We have modified the data by S. K. Freeman and D. O. Landon, Spex Speakers, 8, 4, 1968, by substituting the quantum efficiency of the RCA 31034A PM tube.

a. RCA 31034A photomultiplier.

b. 5000 Å blaze (average of two sets of gratings).

c. Constant luminoxity conditions.

d. A × B × C × D × E = F.

The lost signal can be regained by increasing the amplification factor but with a concomitant loss of S/N which is inversely proportional to $\sqrt{G}$. If sufficient laser power is available or feasible, then the signal may be increased without increasing the gain since $S \propto P_o$. Some of the aforementioned relationships will be employed in the remainder of this chapter as we describe how one obtains a Raman spectrum.

The wavelength at which lasing occurs is controlled by a prism just behind the rear window of the laser tube (see Figure 1.2.). Once the laser has run for 15 minutes or more, the laser output power should be maximized by adjusting the vertical and horizontal controls on the rear of the laser. This is most conveniently accomplished with a power meter.[*] The vertical and horizontal controls adjust the position of the prism and thus allow the operator to select lines of different energy for lasing action. The power output is then maximized by fine adjustment of the vertical and horizontal controls. When changing from a line at one end of the laser spectrum to a line at the other end, it is wise to maximize the output at each intervening line. While these operations are being done, the laser beam should be intercepted by a blackened piece of metal in order to prevent reflections.

Once he laser settings are optimized for a particular wavelength, the laser line must be isolated from the plasma lines by use of an appropriate

---

* A very inexpensive power meter may be constructed by combining a silicon solar cell with an ammeter.

discriminator. Premonochromators[*] are commercially available and have the
advantage of being applicable over a wide wavelength range and of efficiently
isolating any desired laser line.   If you plan to buy one, we recommend that
you verify the energy throughput claimed by the manufacturer.

Interference filters are more convenient and can provide relatively
high throughput.[+] They are somewhat troublesome in that filters are needed
for each laser line and they may allow plasma lines to leak through as they
age. (See Section 4.4.). When using dye lasers that are continuously
tunable, one can extend the range of the interference filter by turning it
at a slight angle to the laser beam.   Since they are generally of the Fabry-
Pérot interference type, this effectively changes the wavelength of maximum
throughput. However, there is a loss of power, so the angle of incidence
should be kept close to 0°.

The wavelength shift can be estimated by

$$\frac{\lambda_a}{\lambda_n} = \frac{\sqrt{n^2 - \sin^2/a}}{n} \qquad (1)$$

where   a = angle of incidence

λ_a = peak wavelength at angle a

λ_n = peak wavelength at normal incidence

n = incidence angle shift factor (or the "effective

index of refraction" of the filter)

---

* Two types of premonochromators are available from Instruments S.A.
  One is the Pellin-Broca type which changes the beam direction by 180
  degrees, and the other is a grating type which causes no change in the
  beam direction.

+ Ditric Optics, Inc., 312 Main Street, Hudson, MA 01749.

The degree to which the peak wavelength is shifted may been seen in Figure 4.1.*

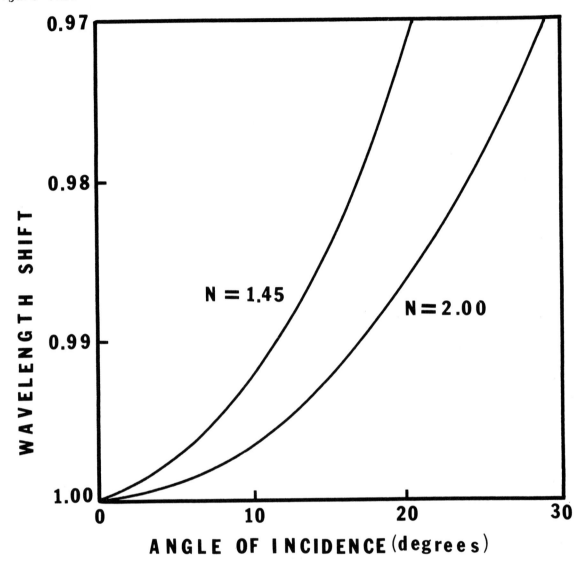

Figure 4.1. Wavelength shift versus angle of incidence for interference filters: N, effective index of filter (reproduced by permission of Oriel Corporation).

---

* Most filters have a highly reflective side and a darker side. For use with laser beams, always place the highly reflective side toward the laser. Failure to do so will cause local heating within the filter and thus reduce its lifetime.

Once the laser line is isolated, the $\Delta\tilde{\nu}$ indicator on the monochromator should be set to read zero at the maximum intensity of the laser line. This procedure must be done with extreme care to prevent damage to the photo-multiplier tube. One method which we have employed is as follows:

1. Turn the laser power down, and set the slit to the lowest possible setting.

2. Insert an empty capillary tube in the sample holder.

3. With the slit closed, move the monochromator setting to a higher energy (absolute wave number) than the desired laser line.

4. Carefully open the slit, and scan across the exciting line. It may be necessary to interpose a few 3 × 5 cards between the capillary tube and the slit to keep the signal on scale.

5. At the maximum of the signal, set $\Delta\tilde{\nu} = 0$.

As stated in Section 1.3, the approximate BP of the instrument is determined manually by adjustment of the slits. The BP for a survey scan need be no smaller than 5 cm^{-1}. This will allow for a relatively rapid scan speed. Thus using the dispersion data supplied with the instrument (see Tables 1.5 and 1.6), the operator calculates the corresponding slit width and sets the slits accordingly. The appropriate setting of the slits is no trivial matter since relevant information can easily be lost (see Figure 1.12).

Next choose the scan speed and time constant (DC operation) or integration time (PC operation). Some instrumentation uses the terms "rise time" or "perios" rather than "time constant." These terms are related by the following equation:

$$5 \times (\text{time constant}) = \text{period} = 2 \times (\text{rise time}) \tag{2}$$

For DC detection the appropriate formula is

$$BP \ (cm^{-1}) \geq \frac{\text{scan speed } (cm^{-1}/\text{min})}{60} \times 4 \ (\text{time constant}) \quad (3)$$

while for PC detection the formula becomes*

$$BP \ (cm^{-1}) \geq \frac{\text{scan speed } (cm^{-1}/\text{min})}{60} \times 4 \ (\text{smooth setting}) \quad (4)$$

Failure to optimize these settings can cause distorted spectra, as illustrated in Figures 1.9 and 1.10. The following are suggested settings for a survey scan over a large wave number range and for a high resolution scan over a small range:

Type	Scan speed	Band Pass	Smooth (or Time Constant)
Survey	250 cm^{-1}/min	5 cm^{-1}	0.3 sec
High Resolution	1 cm^{-1}/min	1 cm^{-1}	15

For convenient reference, Table 4.2 may be employed to select appropriate scan speeds.

---

* For some systems there is an integration setting and a smooth (time constant) control. For optimum results the smooth should be no more than 2 or 3 times the integration time. Increasing the smooth control beyond that level is inadvisable since meaningful data can be lost.

Table 4.2. Maximum Scan Speeds ($\mathring{A}$/min or cm^{-1}/min)

Time Constant	Rise Time (sec)	Period	Spectral Slit Width ($\mathring{A}$ or cm^{-1})				
			1	2	4	8	16
0.1	0.25	0.5	120	250	500	1000	2000
0.25	0.6	1.2	50	100	200	400	800
0.5	1.2	2.5	25	50	100	200	400
1.0	2.5	5.0	12.5	25	50	100	200
2.0	5.0	10.0	6.25	12.5	25	50	100
2.5	6.0	12.0	5	10	25	40	80
5	12	25	2.5	5	10	20	40
10	25	50	1.25	2.5	5	10	20
20	50	100	0.625	1.25	2.5	5	10
25	60	120	0.5	1	2	4	8
50	120	250	0.25	0.5	1	2	4

Source: Reproduced with permission from Spex Industries, Inc.

Finally, before the spectrum is taken, the signal should be maximized by adjusting the positions of the lenses in the optical collection system. The arrangement of these lenses will vary greatly from instrument to instrument, but the general procedure is to bring the incoming beam roughly to focus at the sample position. Then place the sample in an appropriate holder, and move it into the beam. (CAUTION: Always use laser goggles at this point.) Now set the monochromator to the position of one of the bands of the sample. Open the slits and carefully maximize the signal by moving the sample and/or the lenses. Then bring the monochromator to the starting wavelength from about 50 cm^{-1} below to take up backlash, and scan the spectrum.

4.3. DEPOLARIZATION RATIOS

One of the most useful pieces of information that one can obtain from Raman spectra is the depolarization ratio (ρ) of a vibrational mode. The value of this ratio gives an indication as to the symmetry of a vibrational mode and thus is invaluable in making band assignments. Although the calculation of this parameter appears to be a trivial problem, there are a number of important factors to consider.

In the days before the advent of the laser, ρ was defined to be the ratio of the total scattered radiation directed into the monochromator when excited by light polarized perpendicular to the axis of the sample to that excited by light polarized parallel to the sample axis.[*] The values assumed by ρ in this method ranged from 0 to 6/7. Any mode showing a value less than 6/7 was considered to be polarized, and that due to a totally symmetric vibration of a molecule. If one is looking at literature originating before 1970, ρ is likely to range from 0 to 6/7.

The present-day procedure uses polarized incident laser light and analyses the scattered light for that component with polarization parallel to ($I_{\parallel}$) and perpendicular to ($I_{\perp}$) the polarization of the incident light (see Figure 4.2.). The values of ρ_p ($= I_{\perp}/I_{\parallel}$) now can range from 0 to 3/4 under nonresonant conditions (vide infra). Under these conditions only those modes with less than 3/4 are considered to be polarized (see Figure 4.3.).

---

[*] R. S. Tobias, J. Chem. Educ., 44, 2 (1967).

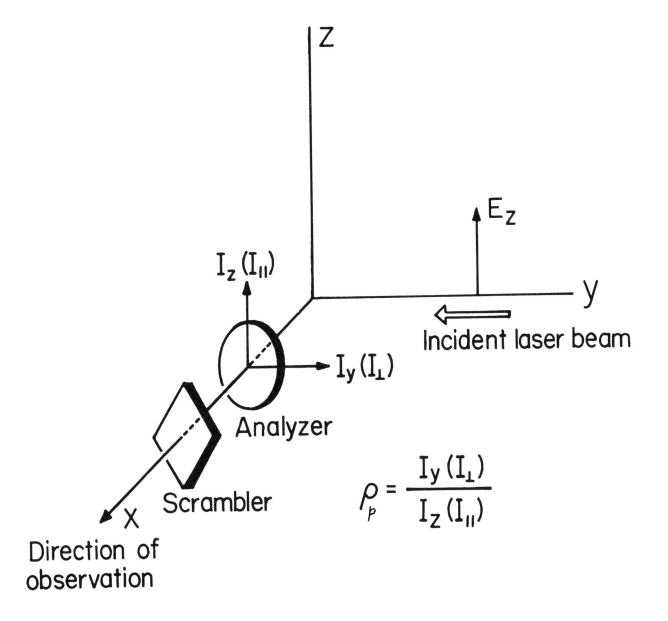

Figure 4.2. Experimental configuration for depolarization measurements.

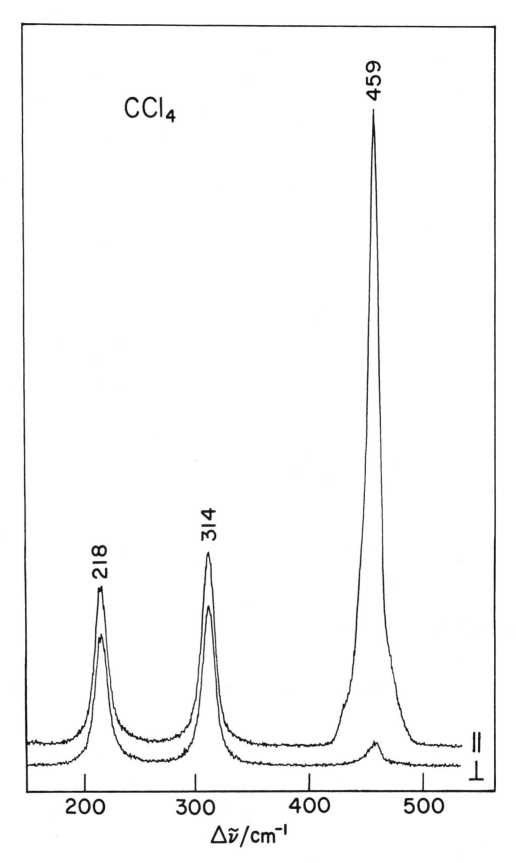

Figure 4.3. Raman spectra of CCl_4 (500–150 cm^{-1}) in the two directions of polarization (488 nm excitation).

When taking data in the manner just described, a "scrambler" must be placed after the analyzer because the monochromator gratings show different efficiencies when interacting with ∥ or ⊥ polarized light.[*] The usual scrambler is simply a quartz wedge whose width varies vertically. However, there is a rather interesting approach that employs liquid crystals.[+] It should also be noted that the slit width has an effect on the value of ρ_p and thus the smallest width convenient should be employed.[‡]

If polarization data are taken when the laser photons are in or approaching resonance with a strong electronic absorption band (resonance Raman scattering), then anomalous or inverse polarization may occur wherein the value of ρ_p may exceed 3/4, and indeed it may approach infinity for systems of very high symmetry (D_{4h}).

For many years it was thought to be impossible to obtain polarization data from colorless microcrystalline materials without using a tedious method

---

[*] As a matter of fact, it is a good idea to leave a scrambler in place while taking a spectrum.

[+] H. Tanji, H. Hamaguchi, H. Matsuura, I. Harada, and T. Shimanouchi, Appl. Spectrosc., 31, 470 (1977).

[‡] F. G. Dijkman and J. H. Van der Maas, Appl. Spectrosc., 30, 545 (1976).
T. G. Spiro and T. C. Strekas, Proc. Nat. Acad. Sci. USA, 69, 2622 (1972).

involving the suspension of the material in a medium having the same refractive index.[*] This difficulty has been overcome by a new technique which involves the addition of CuO or carbon black to the sample and the examination of the spectra using the standard rotating sample technique.[+] The function of these colored additives appears to be that of reducing the depth of penetration of the laser beam and consequently attenuating the amount of reflected or refracted radiation which will have been scrambled with respect to polarization. Figure 4.4 shows the effect of addition of CuO to the 983 cm^{-1} band (totally symmetric mode) of K_2SO_4 powder.

---

[*] P. J. Hendra, "Raman Instrumentation and Sampling," in Laboratory Methods in Infrared Spectroscopy, R. G. Miller, ed (Heyden, London, 1972) p. 247.

[+] D. P. Strommen and K. Nakamoto, Appl. Spectrosc., 37, 436 (1983).

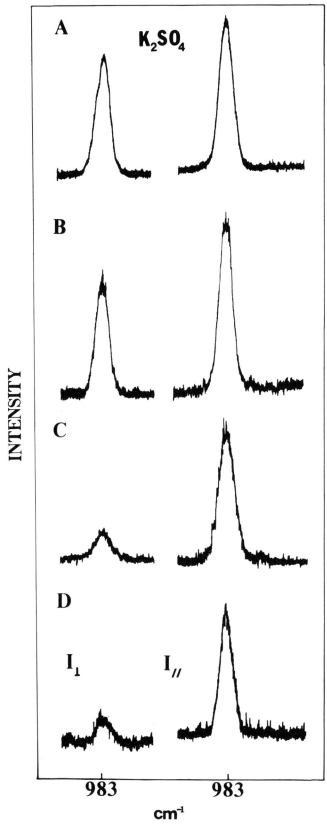

Figure 4.4. Effect of addition of CuO to the polarized Raman spectrum of K_2SO_4:
(a) pure K_2SO_4, (b) 80% K_2SO_4 + 20% CuO, (c) 50% K_2SO_4 + 50% CuO, (d) 20% K_2SO_4 + 80% CuO.

4.4. MISCELLANEOUS PROBLEMS

Two problems often encountered in Raman spectroscopy are discussed in this section: spurious lines and fluorescence.

Spurious Lines

Because premonochromators and optical filters are not 100% efficient in eliminating plasma lines from the incident radiation, spurious lines may appear in the spectrum. These are usually easy to detect since they are typically quite sharp compared to normal Raman bands. Tables 4.3 and 4.4 give the positions of possible spurious lines as a function of the exciting radiation. If a line in a given spectrum is spurious, merely change the exciting line. If it is a real band, it will still be in the spectrum, but it will disappear or shift if it is due to a plasma line. Note that there are also lines from fluorescent lights that may be troublesome. These occur at 2180 cm^{-1} when scanning is set for the 488.0 nm excitation and at 1125 cm^{-1} for the 514.5 nm excitation.

Fluorescence

Fluorescence scattering of light is one of the most troublesome problems for the Raman spectroscopist. The intensity of this type of scattered radiation may be as much as 10^4 greater than the Raman signal. Though it may be said that "everything is fluorescent"[*] there are a number of ways to minimize this problem.

---

[*] T. Hirschfeld, Appl. Spectrosc., 31, 328 (1977).

1. Since in many cases the fluorescence is due to impurities, the sample may be purified. This is usually the most satisfactory method for reducing fluorescence background.

2. The sample can be positioned in front of the collection optics and irradiated (with the slits closed) with high power for a prolonged time. This presumably bleaches the impurities (colorless samples only), and the technique is most effective when the sample is stationary.

3. Quenching agents such as potassium iodide (solution) or mercury halides (vapor phase) may be added.[*]

4. A mode-lock laser may be employed, and single photon-counting techniques may be used to achieve time discrimination.[+]

5. Repetitive scanning and background subtraction may be employed.[‡]

Needless to say, methods 1 and 2 are not applicable if the sample itself is fluorescent. In that event switching of the exciting wavelength should be tried before methods 3 through 5 are employed.

---

[*] For the potassium iodide case, see J. M. Friedman and R. M. Hochstrasser, Chem. Phys. Lett., 33, 225 (1975); for the vapor phase case, see V. A. Maroni and P. T. Cunningham, Appl. Spectrosc., 27, 428 (1973).

[+] R. P. Van Duyne, D. L. Jeanmaire, and D. F. Shriver, Anal. Chem., 46, 213, (1974).

[‡] T. M. Loehr, W. E. Keyes and P. A. Pincus, Anal. Biochem., 96, 456 (1979).

Table 4.3. Apparent Raman Displacement of Emission Lines from Argon-ion Exciting Radiation (cm^{-1})

Wavelength in Air (nm)	Peak Height	457.9 nm	465.8 nm	472.7 nm	476.5 nm	488.0 nm	496.5 nm	501.7 nm	514.5 nm
458.94	530	48							
459.87	15	92							
460.96	819	143							
463.76	74	274							
465.79	366	368							
472.68	500	681	313						
473.22	23	705	337	24					
473.62	800	723	355	42					
476.49	470	850	482	169					
480.57	1150	1028	660	347	178				
484.76	840	1208	840	527	358				
486.55	40	1284	916	603	434				
487.98	1600	1344	976	663	494				
488.86	90	1381	1013	700	531	37			
490.44	60	1447	1079	766	597	103			
493.28	460	1564	1196	883	714	220			
494.28	10	1605	1237	924	755	261			
496.51	530	1696	1328	1015	846	352			
497.20	270	1724	1356	1043	874	380	28		
500.89	830	1872	1504	1191	1022	528	176		
501.72	330	1905	1537	1224	1055	561	209		
506.19	790	2081	1713	1400	1231	737	385	176	
509.05	5	2192	1824	1511	1342	848	496	287	
514.15	27	2387	2019	1706	1537	1043	691	482	
514.52	95	2401	2033	1720	1551	1057	705	496	
516.28	7	2467	2099	1786	1617	1123	771	562	66
516.57	21	2478	2110	1797	1628	1134	782	573	77
517.64	26	2518	2150	1837	1668	1174	822	613	117
518.82	3	2562	2194	1881	1712	1218	866	657	161

Table 4.3. Continued

Wavelength in Air (nm)	Peak Height	457.9 nm	465.8 nm	472.7 nm	476.5 nm	488.0 nm	496.5 nm	501.7 nm	514.5 nm
521.69	8	2688	2300	1987	1818	1324	972	763	267
528.70	75	2922	2554	2241	2072	1578	1226	1017	521
530.58	4	2989	2621	2308	2139	1645	1293	1084	588
539.78	4	3310	2942	2629	2460	1966	1614	1405	909
540.30	3	3328	2960	2647	2478	1984	1632	1423	927
540.77	4	3344	2976	2663	2494	2000	1648	1439	943
545.22	3	3495	3127	2814	2645	2151	1799	1590	1094
545.43	6	3502	3134	2821	2652	2158	1806	1597	1101
549.60	7	3641	3273	2960	2791	2297	1945	1736	1240
549.81	3		3280	2967	2798	2304	1952	1743	1247
550.05	3		3288	2975	2806	2312	1960	1751	1255
555.90	10		3479	3166	2997	2503	2151	1942	1446
557.26	4		3523	3210	3041	2547	2195	1986	1490
560.70	12		3633	3320	3151	2657	2305	2096	1600
565.07	8			3458	3289	2795	2443	2234	1738
565.45	3			3470	3301	2807	2455	2246	1750
572.51	3			3688	3519	3025	2673	2464	1968
573.99	3				3564	3070	2718	2509	2013
577.27	7				3663	3169	2817	2608	2112
578.71	3					3212	2860	2651	2155
581.34	5					3290	2938	2729	2233
584.43	4					3331	3029	2820	2324
586.07	3					3429	3077	2868	2372
588.31	5					3494	3142	2933	2437
588.87	11					3510	3158	2949	2453
591.24	19					3578	3226	3017	2521
592.92	6					3626	3274	3065	2569
598.60	6						3434	3225	2729
598.96	6						3444	3235	2739

Table 4.3. Continued

Wavelengths in Air (nm)	Peak Height	457.9 nm	465.8 nm	472.7 nm	476.5 nm	488.0 nm	496.5 nm	501.7 nm	514.5 nm
603.26	48						3563	3354	2858
604.39	16						3594	3385	2889
605.34	8						3620	3411	2915
605.97	15							3428	2932
607.77	6							3477	2981
609.92	5							3535	3039
610.41	44							3548	3052
611.53	1020							3578	3082
612.43	47							3602	3106
613.93	51								3146
614.61	8								3164
615.59	4								3190
617.27	950								3234
618.76	12								3273
620.21	5								3311
621.29	9								3339
621.64	6								3348
624.05	17								3410
624.32	470								3417
629.71	9								3554
630.82	14								3582
632.50	13								3624

Source: R. O. Kagel, "Raman Spectroscopy" in CRC Handbook of Spectroscopy, Vol. 2, J. W. Robinson, ed. (CRC Press, Boca Raton, Fla., 1974).

Table 4.4. Apparent Raman Displacement of Emission Lines from Krypton Ion Exciting Radiation (cm^{-1})

Wavelength in Air (nm)	Peak Height	530.8 nm	568.2 nm	647.1 nm	676.4 nm	752.4 nm
532.80	200	50				
533.34	2000	88				
534.68	300	134				
535.55	80	165				
541.84	200	382				
543.86	400	450				
544.63	900	476				
546.82	1100	550				
549.95	450	654				
552.29	1050	731				
555.30	400	829				
556.22	200	859				
556.86	1000	879				
557.03	550	885				
563.50	1400	1091				
565.04	250	1139				
566.99	300	1200				
567.28	570	1209				
567.45	400	1214				
568.19	3500	1237				
569.03	2000	1263	26			
569.41	400	1275	38			
569.98	400	1293	56			
571.72	180	1346	109			
575.30	1000	1455	218			
577.14	1700	1510	273			
577.80	400	1530	293			
586.07	270	1773	536			
587.09	750	1804	567			

Table 4.4. Continued

Wavelength in Air (nm)	Peak Height	530.8 nm	568.2 nm	647.1 nm	676.4 nm	752.4 nm
591.17	110	1921	684			
596.75	100	2079	842			
599.22	1000	2148	911			
601.00	90	2198	961			
602.24	200	2232	995			
603.72	10	2392	1155			
609.45	50	2428	1191			
611.96	70	2495	1258			
616.88	160	2625	1388			
630.37	160	2972	1735			
631.28	10	2995	1758			
639.11	100	3190	1953			
640.98	70	3235	1998			
641.66	150	3251	2014			
624.02	700	3260	2023			
647.09	250	3381	2144			
651.09	430	3478	2241	97		
657.01	1000	3618	2381	236		
660.30	160		2454	310		
662.50	30		2505	360		
662.86	160		2513	368		
663.50	110		2528	383		
664.45	100		2549	405		
665.25	100		2567	423		
668.40	60		2600	495		
676.44	330		2816	671		
677.12	100		2831	686	15	
687.08	110		3045	900	229	
694.41	30		3198	1053	382	

Table 4.4. Continued

Wavelength in Air (nm)	Peak Height	530.8 nm	568.2 nm	647.1 nm	676.4 nm	752.4 nm
707.40	100		3463	1318	647	
713.40	170		3593	1448	777	
721.31	600			1590	919	
728.98	900			1736	1065	
731.05	80			1771	1100	
733.78	60			1827	1156	
736.16	90			1871	1200	
737.30	60			1894	1223	
740.70	800			1953	1282	
743.58	400			2006	1335	
744.38	150			2020	1349	
748.68	280			2097	1426	
749.36	180			2109	1438	
751.26	400			2144	1473	
752.45	600			2164	1493	
755.57	180			2220	1549	56
756.54	250			2237	1566	73
758.74	550			2274	1603	110
760.15	600			2299	1628	135
768.52	400			2442	1771	278
769.45	250			2458	1787	294
773.57	200			2528	1857	364
775.07	200			2553	1882	389
778.94	130			2617	1946	453
781.25	250			2655	1984	491
782.60	450			2677	2006	513
783.58	190			2693	2022	529
784.07	520			2701	2030	537
785.48	500			2724	2053	560
790.76	120			2807	2136	643

Table 4.4. Continued

Wavelength in Air (nm)	Peak Height	530.8 nm	568.2 nm	647.1 nm	676.4 nm	752.4 nm
791.04	190			2813	2142	649
791.45	70			2820	2149	656
793.14	130			2847	2176	683
797.36	100			2914	2243	750
799.32	700			2944	2273	780
799.80	300			2952	2281	788
801.86	110			2984	2313	320
805.95	600			3047	2376	883
807.50	100			3072	2401	908
808.80	550			3092	2421	928
810.44	700			3116	2445	952
811.29	1500			3129	2468	965
813.00	700			3155	2484	991
813.40	200			3162	2491	998
813.90	100			3169	2498	1005
814.51	300			3178	2507	1014
817.70	700			3226	2555	1062
819.00	600			3245	2574	1081
820.27	600			3264	2593	1100
820.80	550			3272	2601	1108
822.90	500			3295	2624	1131
826.32	700			3353	2682	1189
828.10	600			3379	2708	1215
828.90	600			3392	2721	1228
829.81	600			3404	2733	1240
836.90	200			3506	2835	1342
841.25	50			3568	2897	1404
843.80	80			3603	2932	1439
847.33	200				2981	1488
850.20	400				3021	1528
850.89	450				3031	1538
851.86	85				3044	1551
853.68	180				3069	1576

Source: C. Jilien and C. Hirlimann, J. Raman Spec. 9, 62 (1980).

CHAPTER 5. TYPICAL SOLVENT SPECTRA

The Raman spectra of 20 most commonly encountered laboratory solvents as well as some of their deuterated analogs are presented in Figures 5.1 through 5.19. See Table 5.1 for a complete listing. We have also included the spectra of a few inorganic ions that can be used as internal standards. See Table 5.2 for a complete listing of these.

The spectra were obtained in our laboratory using a Spex Model 1401 double monochromator, a Spectra-Physics Model 164 Ar-ion laser, an RCA 31034A photomultiplier tube along with a Spex DPC-2 photon-counting system. Typical instrument settings were the following:

1. Laser wavelength: 488.0 nm.

2. Laser power (before optics): 100 mW.

3. Slits: 200/300/200.

4. High voltage: 1730.

5. Counts (full scale): 5 K.

6. Integration: 0.2 sec.

7. Scan speed: 50 cm^{-1}/min.

8. Recorder speed: 1 in./min.

9. Temperature: ambient.

All samples were purified prior to taking the spectra and were run in NMR tubes.

Since the solvents listed in this chapter are frequently used in the preparation and purification of many compounds, and thus may be retained by the products, we have compiled a list of the positions of their strongest bands as a convenient reference (see Table 5.3.). Thus, if a researcher

observes a spurious Raman band in a spectrum, he or she may conveniently

look up the spectra of possible contaminants and verify or disprove its

presence. For example, if a band is found at $\sim$992 cm^{-1}, the table indicates

that benzene or pyridine may be present. If neither one was used in the

preparation or purification of the compound, then the band is probably due

to the compound itself. On the other hand, if pyridine was used, there

should be a second band at $\sim$1030 cm^{-1}.

Internal standards are necessary for quantitative work due to the nature

of the Raman effect. Peak heights will be sensitive to the refractive index

of the solvent, the laser power at the sample, the slit width, the frequency

of the exciting line, the efficiency of the gratings at the scattered

frequency, and the properties of the cell in which the sample is contained.

A more complete discussion of the techniques involved in quantitative work was

presented in Section 3.2. Suffice it to say at this point that an internal

standard is required for quantitative treatment of intensities. In some cases

the solvents themselves supply the internal reference bands. However, when

water is the solvent, the standard must be added because water itself is

a weak Raman scatterer. (It is this property that makes Raman the ideal

technique for studying aqueous solutions.) Table 5.4 lists the major bands

of some relatively inert water soluble compounds that have been or may be

used as internal standards when water is the solvent. These compounds may

also be used as internal standards for solid state measurements.

Table 5.1. Index to Solvent Spectra

Solvent	Figure Number	Reference
Chloroform	5.1A	1
d_1-Chloroform	5.1B	1
Diethyl ether	5.2A	2
n-Hexane	5.2B	3
Carbon tetrachloride	5.3A	4
Carbon disulfide	5.3B	5
Dimethylsulfoxide	5.4A	6
d_6-Dimethylsulfoxide	5.4B	6
Methylene chloride	5.5A	7
1,2-Dichloroethane	5.5B	8
Indene (also see Table 3.1).	5.6A	9
Dimethyl formamide	5.6B	10
Acetone	5.7A	11
d_6-Acetone	5.7B	11
Toluene	5.8A	12
Cyclohexane	5.8B	13
Tetrahydrofuran	5.9A	14
1,4-Dioxane	5.9B	15
Ethanol	5.10A	16
Methanol	5.10B	17
Nitromethane	5.11A	18
Acetonitrile	5.11B	19
Pyridine	5.12A	20
d_5-Pyridine	5.12B	20
Benzene	5.13A	21
d_6-Benzene	5.13B	21

Table 5.2. Index to Raman Spectra of Inorganic Reference Materials

Compound	Figure Number	Reference
Sodium tungstate dihydrate (s)	5.14A	22
Basic lead sulfate (s)	5.14B	22
Sodium cacodylate (s)	5.15A	22
Sodium cacodylate (aq)	5.15B	23
Potassium perchlorate (aq)	5.16A	24
Potassium periodate (s)	5.16B	22
Sodium molybdate dihydrate (s)	5.17A	22
Sodium molybdate (aq)	5.17B	24
Potassium sulfate (s)	5.18A	22
Potassium sulfate (aq)	5.18B	24
Potassium nitrate (s)	5.19A	22
Potassium nitrate (aq)	5.19B	25

Note: The abbreviations in parentheses are S for solid, aq for aqueous
solution.

Table 5.3. Characteristic Bands (2500 cm^{-1}) of Common Laboratory Solvents

Solvent	Strongest Band (cm^{-1})	Confirmatory Bands	Figure Number	Reference
d$_1$-Chloroform	365	649, 262	5.1B	1
Diethyl ether	439	—	5.2A	2
Carbon tetrachloride	460	314, 214	5.3A	4
d$_6$-Dimethlsulfoxide	617	2125, 2249	5.4B	6
1,2-Dichloroethane	654	754, 300	5.5B	8
Carbon disulfide	656	—	5.3B	5
Dimetyl formamide	662	868	5.6B	10
Chloroform	668	366, 262	5.1A	1
Dimethylsulfoxide	669	697	5.4A	6
Methylene chloride	700	284	5.5A	7
Acetone	786	—	5.7A	11
Cyclohexane	802	—	5.8B	13
1,4-Dioxane	835	—	5.9B	15
Ethanol	877	—	5.10A	16
Tetrahydrofuran	913	—	5.9A	14
Nitromethane	921	—	5.11A	17
d$_5$-Pyridine	962	—	5.12B	19
d$_6$-Benzene	943	2293	5.13B	20
Benzene	992	—	5.13A	20
Pyridine	992	1030	5.12A	19
Toluene	1004	784, 1029	5.8A	12
Methanol	1033	—	5.10B	16
d$_6$-Acetone	2108	695	5.7B	11
Acetonitrile	2249	—	5.11B	18

Note: Solvents arranged in order of increasing frequency of strongest band.

Table 5.4. Index to Major Peaks (cm^{-1}) of Useful Inorganic Compounds

Compound	Strongest Band	Figure Number	Reference
Basic lead sulfate (s)	150	5.14B	22
Sodium cacodylate (s)	599	5.15A	22
Sodium cacodylate (aq)	608	5.15B	23
Potassium periodate (s)	789	5.16B	22
Sodium molybdate (aq)	894	5.17B	24
Sodium molybdate dihydrate (s)	895	5.17A	22
Potassium perchlorate (aq)	928	5.16A	24
Sodium tungstate dihydrate (s)	931	5.14A	22
Potassium sulfate (s)	975	5.18A	22
Potassium sulfate (aq)	981	5.18B	24
Potassium nitrate (aq)	1050	5.19B	25
Potassium nitrate (s)	1055	5.19A	22

Note: In parentheses, s for solid and aq for aqueous solution.

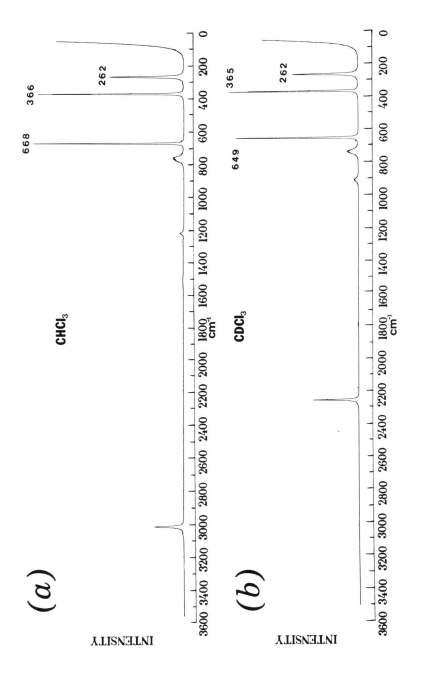

Figure 5.1

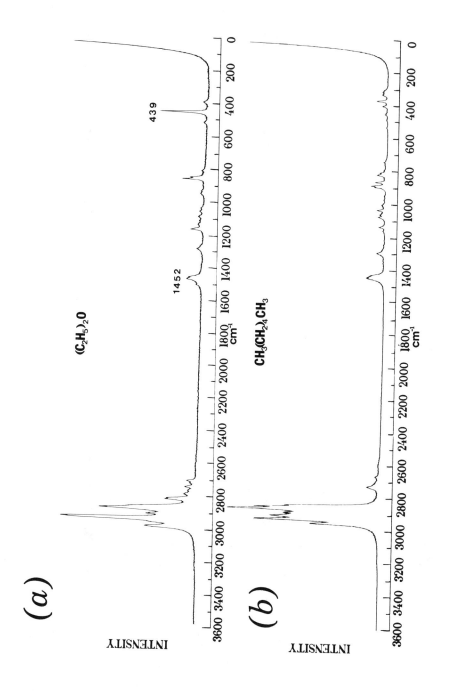

Figure 5.2

110

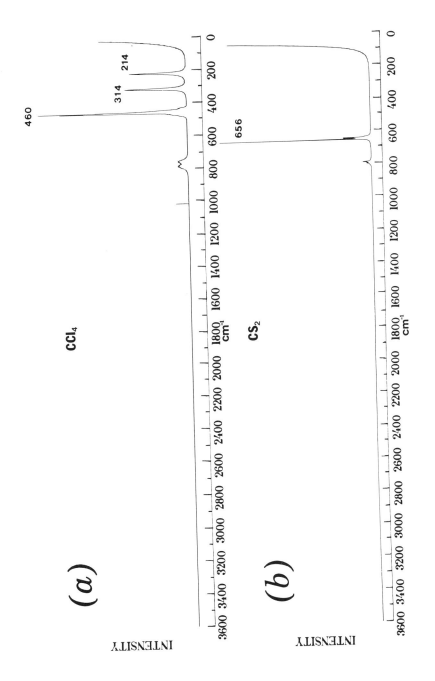

CCl₄

(a)

CS₂

(b)

Figure 5.3

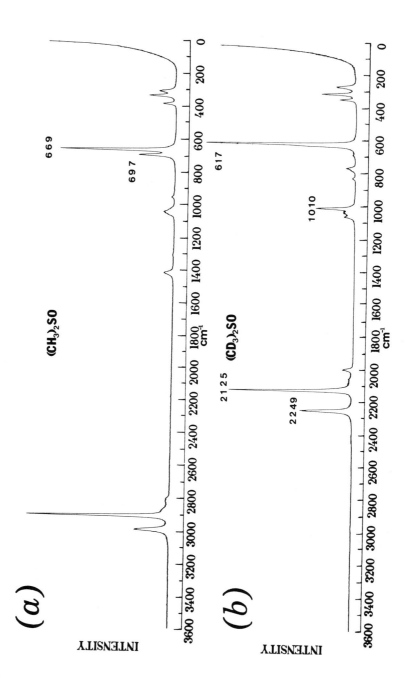

Figure 5.4

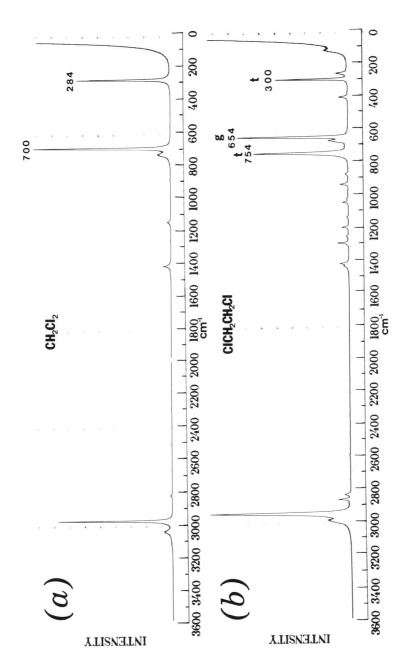

Figure 5.5

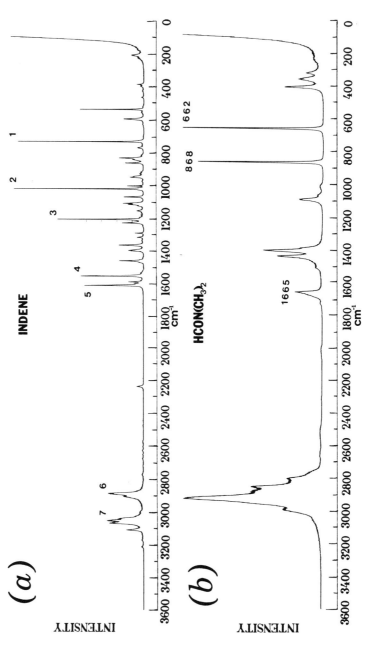

Figure 5.6

114

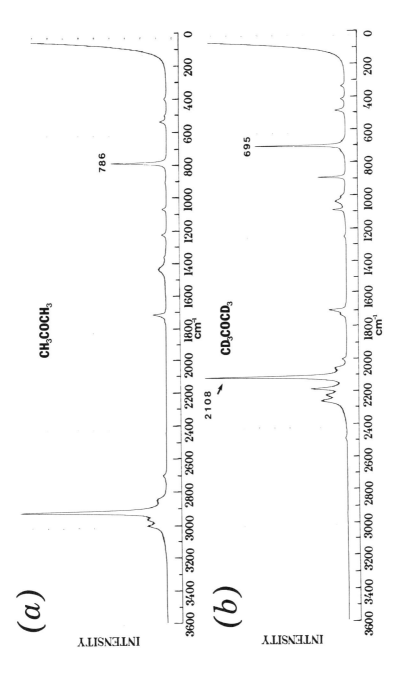

Figure 5.7

115

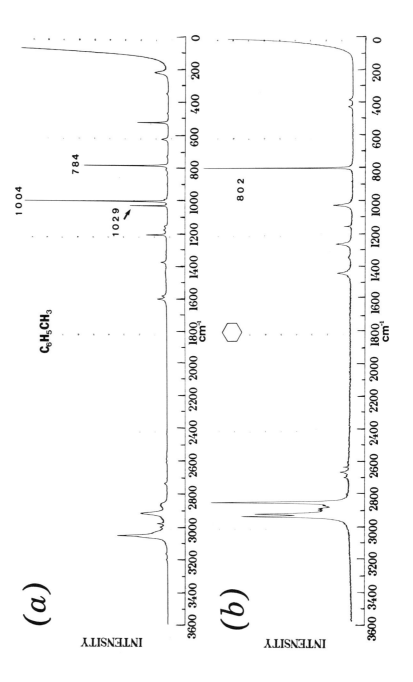

Figure 5.8

116

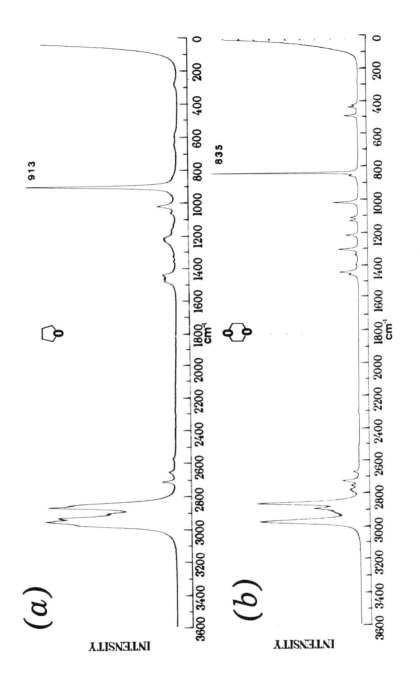

Figure 5.9

117

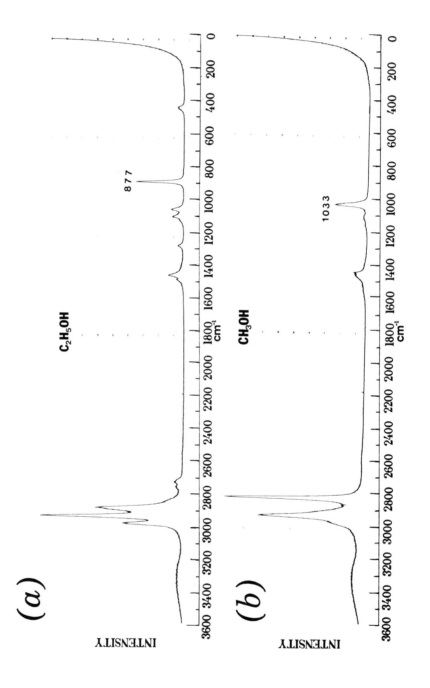

Figure 5.10

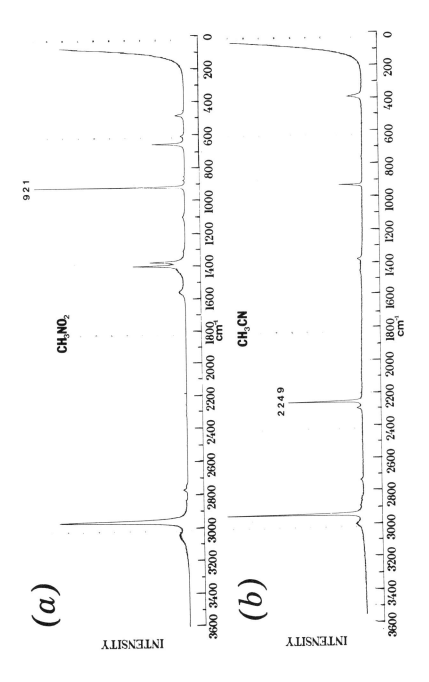

Figure 5.11

119

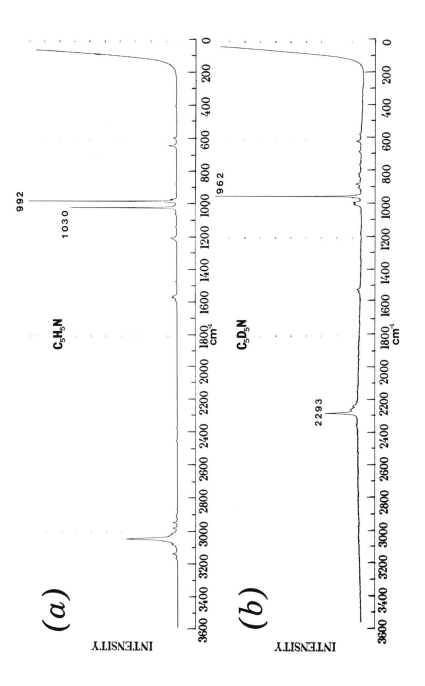

Figure 5.12

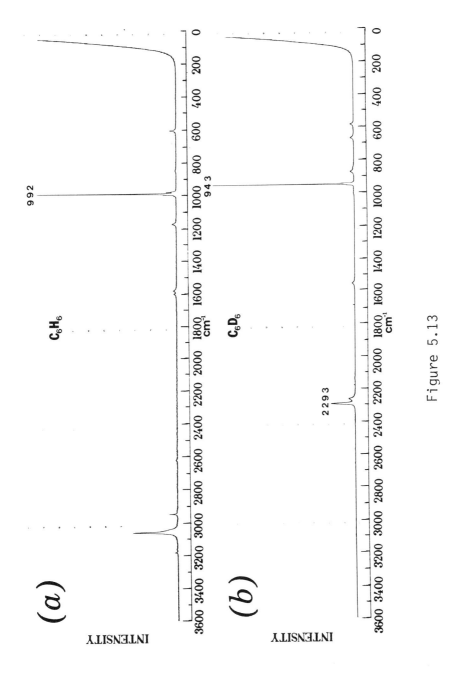

Figure 5.13

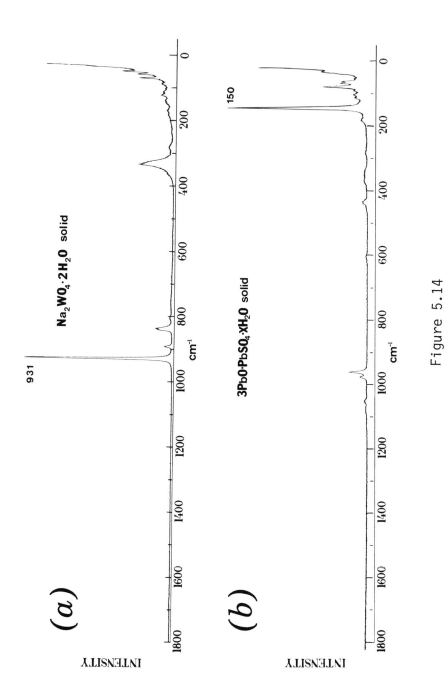

(a)

Na₂WO₄·2H₂O solid

931

cm⁻¹

INTENSITY

(b)

3PbO·PbSO₄·xH₂O solid

150

cm⁻¹

INTENSITY

Figure 5.14

122

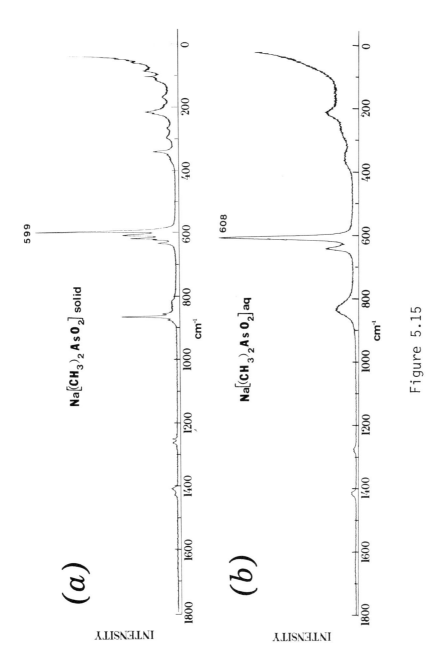

Figure 5.15

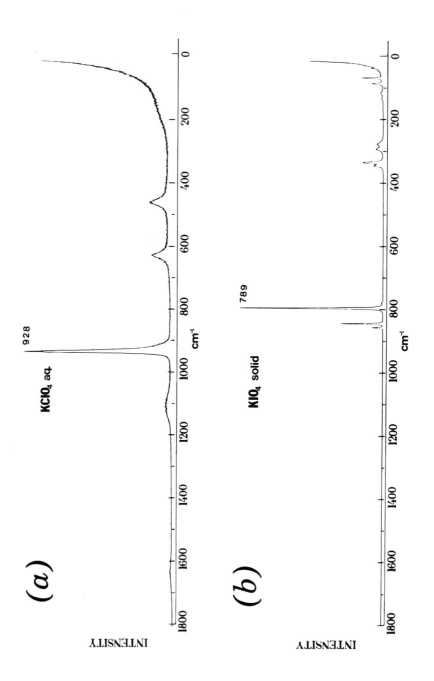

Figure 5.16

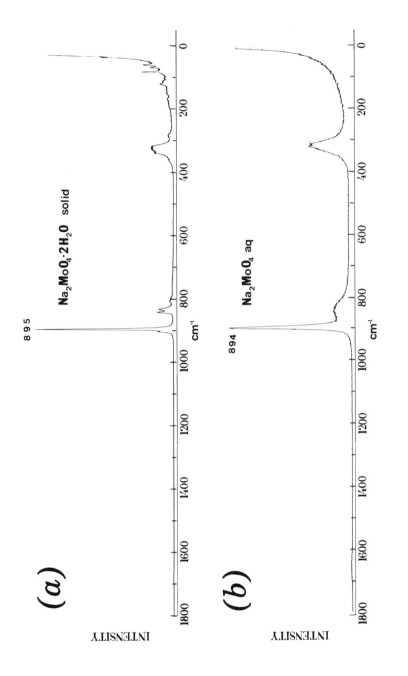

Figure 5.17

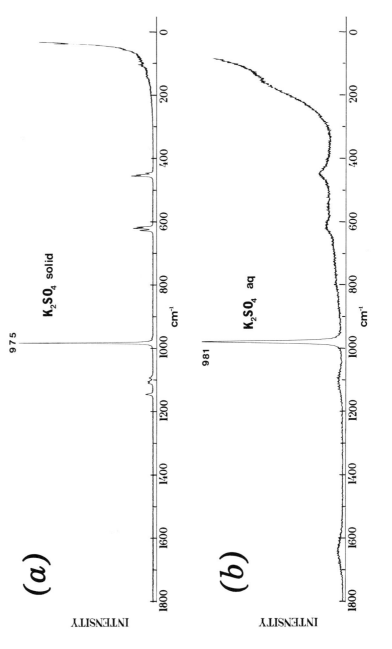

Figure 5.18

126

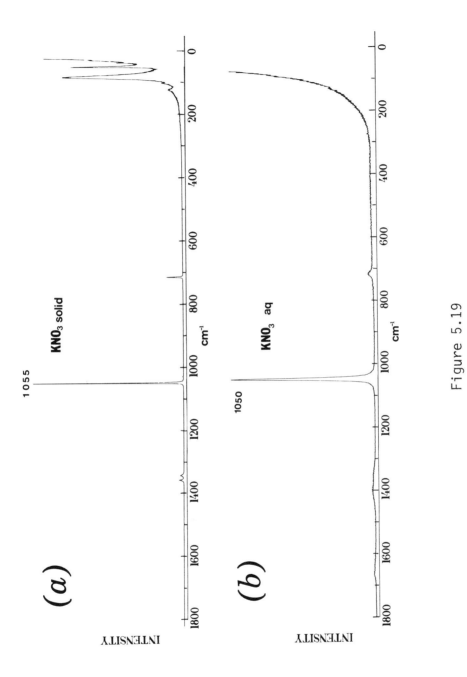

Figure 5.19

References for Tables 5.1. and 5.2.

1. J. R. Madigan and F. F. Cleveland, J. Chem. Phys., 18, 1081 (1950); H. Siebert, Z. anorg. u. allgem. chem., 273, 21 (1953).

2. F. F. Cleveland, M. J. Murray, H. H. Haney, and J. Shackelford, J. Chem. Phys., 8, 153 (1940).

3. This laboratory.

4. R. J. H. Clark and P. D. Mitchell, J. Chem. Soc., Faraday (II), 71, 515 (1975).

5. This laboratory.

6. M.-T. Forel and M. Tranquille, Spectrochim. Acta, 26A, 1023 (1970).

7. C. Corin and G. B. B. M. Sutherland, Proc. Roy. Soc., 165, 43 (1938).

8. J. K. Brown and N. Sheppard, Trans. Farad. Soc., 48, 128 (1952).

9. P. J. Hendra and E. J. Loader, Chem. Ind., 718 (1968).

10. Characteristic Raman Frequencies of Organic Compounds, F. R. Dollish, W. G. Fately, and F. F. Bentley, Wiley Interscience, New York, 1974, p. 126.

11. G. Dellepiane and J. Overend, Spectrochim. Acta, 22, 593 (1966).

12. J. Goubeau and E. Köhler, Chem. Ber., 75, 65 (1942).

13. R. S. Rasmussen, J. Chem. Phys., 11, 249 (1943).

14. H. Tschamler and H. Voetter, Monatsch. Chem., 83, 302 (1952).

15. F. E. Malherbe and H. J. Bernstein, J. Am. Chem. Soc., 74, 4408 (1952).

16. This laboratory

17. S. Mizushima, Y. Morino, and G. Okamoto, Bull. Chem. Soc. Japan, 11, 698 (1936).

18. A. J. Wells and E. B. Wilson, Jr., J. Chem. Phys., 9, 314 (1941).

19. H. W. Thompson and R. L. Williams, Trans. Faraday Soc., 48, 502 (1952).

20. L. Corsin, B. J. Fax, and R. C. Lord, J. Chem. Phys., 21, 1170 (1953).

21. N. Herzfeld, C. K. Ingold, and H. G. Poole, J. Chem. Soc., 316 (1946).

22. This laboratory.

23. D. C. Blazej and W. L. Peticolas, Proc. Natl. Acad. Sci. USA, 74, 2639 (1977).

24. S. D. Ross, Inorganic Infrared and Raman Spectra, McGraw-Hill, New York, 1972, p. 216.

25. R. K. Khanna, J. Lingscheid and J. C. Decius, Spectrochim. Acta, 20, 1109 (1964).

GENERAL REFERENCES

INTRODUCTORY RAMAN SPECTROSCOPY

1. T. R. Gilson and P. J. Hendra, <u>Laser Raman Spectroscopy</u>, Wiley, New York, 1970,

2. L. A. Woodward, <u>Introduction to the Theory of Molecular Vibrations and Vibrational Spectroscopy</u>, Oxford University Press, Oxford, 1972.

3. C. N. Banwell, <u>Fundamentals of Molecular Spectroscopy</u>, 2d ed. McGraw-Hill, New York, 1972.

4. N. B. Colthup, L. H. Daly and S. E. Wiberley, Introduction to Infrared and Raman Spectroscopy, 2d ed., Academic Press, New York, 1974.

5. J. G. Grasselli, M. K. Snavely and B. J. Bulkin, <u>Chemical Applications of Raman Spectroscopy</u>, Wiley, New York, 1981.

EXPERIMENTAL RAMAN SPECTROSCOPY

1. E. J. Loader, <u>Basic Laser Raman Spectroscopy</u>, Heyden, London, 1970.

2. M. C. Tobin, <u>Laser Raman Spectroscopy</u>, Wiley-Interscience, New York, 1971.

3. P. J. Hendra, "Raman Instrumentation and Sampling" in <u>Laboratory Methods in Infrared Spectroscopy</u>, R. G. J. Miller, ed., Heyden, London, 1972.

130

THEORY OF RAMAN SPECTROSCOPY

1. G. Herzberg, <u>Molecular Spectra and Molecular Structure; Infrared and Raman Spectra of Polyatomic Molecules</u>, Vol. 2. Van Nostrand, Princeton, 1945.

2. G. Herzberg, <u>Molecular Spectra and Molecular Structure; Spectra of Diatomic Molecules</u>, Vol. 1. Van Nostrand, Princeton, 1950.

3. E. B. Wilson, J. C. Decius, and P. C. Cross, <u>Molecular Vibrations</u>. McGraw-Hill, New York, 1955.

4. H. A. Szymanski, ed. <u>Raman Spectroscopy: Theory and Practice</u>, Vols. 1 and 2. Plenum Press, New York, 1967 and 1970.

5. D. Steele, <u>Theory of Vibrational Spectroscopy</u>, Saunders, Philadelphia, 1971.

6. J. A. Konigstein, <u>Introduction to the Theory of the Raman Effect</u>. D. Reidel, Dordrecht, Holland, 1973.

7. D. A. Long, <u>Raman Spectroscopy</u>. McGraw-Hill, New York, 1977.

APPLICATION OF RAMAN SPECTROSCOPY TO ORGANIC COMPOUNDS

1. F. R. Dollish, W. G. Fateley, and F. F. Bentley, <u>Characteristic Raman Frequencies of Organic Compounds</u>. Wiley, New York, 1974.

2. B. Schrader and W. Meier, eds., <u>Raman and Infrared Atlas of Organic Compounds</u>, Vols. 1 and 2. Verlag Chemie, Weinheim, 1974 and 1975.

Applications of Raman Spectroscopy to Inorganic, Organometallic and Coordination Compounds

1. _Spectroscopic Properties of Inorganic and Organometallic Compounds_, Vol. 1 (1968) to the present. The Chemical Society, London.

2. _Molecular Spectroscopy_—Specialist Periodical Reports, Vol. 1 (1973) to the present. The Chemical Society, London.

3. N. N. Greenwood, E. J. F. Ross, and B. P. Straughan, _Index of Vibrational Spectra of Inorganic and Organometallic Compounds_, Vols. 1 and 2. Butterworths, London, 1972, 1976.

4. S. D. Ross, _Inorganic Infrared and Raman Spectra_. McGraw-Hill, New York, 1972.

5. K. Nakamoto, _Infrared and Raman Spectra of Inorganic and Coordination Compounds_, 3d ed., Wiley, New York, 1978.

6. E. Maslowsky, Jr., _Vibrational Spectra of Organometallic Compounds_. Wiley, New York, 1976.

Advances in Raman Spectroscopy

1. R. J. H. Clark and R. E. Hester, eds. _Advances in Infrared and Raman Spectroscopy_, Vol. 1 (1973) to the present. Heyden, London

2. J. Durig, ed. _Vibrational Spectra and Structure_, Vol. 1 (1972) to the present. Elsevier, Amsterdam.

3. J. P. Mathieu, ed. _Advances in Raman Spectroscopy_, Vol. 1. Heyden, London, 1973.

4. C. B. Moore, ed. _Chemical and Biochemical Applications of Lasers_, Vol. 1 (1974) to the present. Academic Press, New York.

Review Articles

1. L. A. Woodward, "Application of Raman Spectroscopy to Inorganic Chemistry." Quart. Rev., 10, 185 (1956).

2. R. S. Tobias, "Raman Spectroscopy in Inorganic Chemistry." J. Chem. Educ., 44, 2 and 70 (1967).

3. B. Schrader, "Chemical Applications of Raman Spectroscopy." Angew. Chem. (Int. Ed.), 12, 884 (1973).

4. W. Kiefer, "Laser-Excited Resonance Raman Spectra of Small Molecules and Ions—A Review." Appl. Spectrosc., 28, 115 (1974).

5. I. R. Beattie, "Vibrational Infrared and Raman Spectroscopy in Inorganic Chemistry." Chem. Soc. Rev., 4, 167 (1975).

6. D. P. Strommen and K. Nakamoto, "Resonance Raman Spectroscopy." J. Chem. Educ., 54, 474 (1977).

7. C. F. Shaw, III, "Resonance Fluorescence and Resonance Raman Spectroscopy of Bromine and Iodine Vapor." J. Chem. Educ., 58, 343 (1981).

8. G. A. Ozin, "Single Crystal and Gas Phase Raman Spectroscopy in Inorganic Chemistry." Prog. Inorg. Chem., 14, 173 (1971).

9. H. Yamada, "Resonance Raman Spectroscopy of Adsorbed Species on Solid Surfaces." Appl. Spectrosc. Rev., 17, 227 (1981).

Special Topics

1. G. Turrell, <u>Infrared and Raman Spectra of Crystals</u>. Academic Press, New York, 1972.

2. W. G. Fateley, F. R. Dollish, N. T. McDevitt, and F. F. Bentley, <u>Infrared and Raman Selection Rules for Molecular and Lattice Vibrations: The Correlation Method</u>. Wiley—Interscience, New York, 1972.

3. H. E. Hallam, ed. <u>Vibrational Spectroscopy of Trapped Species</u>. Wiley, New York, 1973.

4. M. Moskovits and G. A. Ozin, <u>Cryochemistry</u>. Wiley, New York, 1976.

5. A. Weber, ed. <u>Raman Spectroscopy of Gases and Liquids</u>. Springer-Verlag, New York, 1978.

6. R. K. Chang and T. E. Furtak, eds. <u>Surface Enhanced Raman Scattering</u>. Plenum Press, New York, 1982.

Underlined page numbers refer to tables and figures.

DATE DUE
DATE DE RETOUR

Hol			

LOWE-MARTIN No. 1137